Grade 6

Practice Book B

A

Published by Macmillan/McGraw-Hill, of McGraw-Hill Education, a division of The McGraw-Hill Companies, Inc., Two Penn Plaza, New York, New York 10121.

Printed in the United States of America

2 3 4 5 6 7 8 9 10 079 09 08 07 06

Contents

Unit 1 • Take Action

Unit 2 • Saving the Day

Unit 3 • Great Ideas

Unit 4 • Achievements

Unit 5 • Turning Points

Unit 6 • Yesterday, Today, and Tomorrow

Name ______________________________

Replace each vocabulary word that is in parentheses with an appropriate synonym or definition.

Charlie was missing. Hundreds of volunteers gathered to help search through the woods to find him. My friend Doug and I joined a group of volunteers in a field near the Main Street and Chestnut Road (intersection) (**1.**) ________________. The principal of our school, Ms. Kendall, explained the search (procedure) (**2.**) ________________ to us. She was telling everyone about Charlie when she (abruptly) (**3.**) ________________ stopped speaking. I was (conscious) (**4.**) ________________ of people in the crowd sniffling, and I could tell that Ms. Kendall, was about to cry, too. Then, Ms. Kendall sent us off to search.

When we entered the woods, (anxiety) (**5.**) ________________ was high. As we walked, the deep shadows of the trees began to (engulf) (**6.**) ________________ us.

About an hour into our search, we heard Charlie calling out to his sister. I was so excited that I slipped going down a hill and slid to the bottom in a (cascade) (**7.**) ________________ of leaves. A scrape on my hand is my (souvenir) (**8.**) ________________ of this adventure. But learning that Charlie was safe at last made it worth all the trouble.

Name ____

Plan a story about a person who takes action to right a wrong or to protect and save a person or animal. Then fill in the chart to organize your ideas for the story.

Element	Story Title	
Character	Main Character's Name	
	Traits	
	Other Character Names	
	Character Traits:	
Setting(s)	When:	
	Where:	
Plot	Problem:	
	Solution:	
	Conclusion:	

Now use the information in your chart to write your story. Use another sheet of paper if you need to.

At Home: Choose one of the story elements of a book, movie, or TV show that everyone has seen. Then discuss how that element contributed to the story.

Name ____________________

As you read *The Summer of the Swans*, fill in the Story Map.

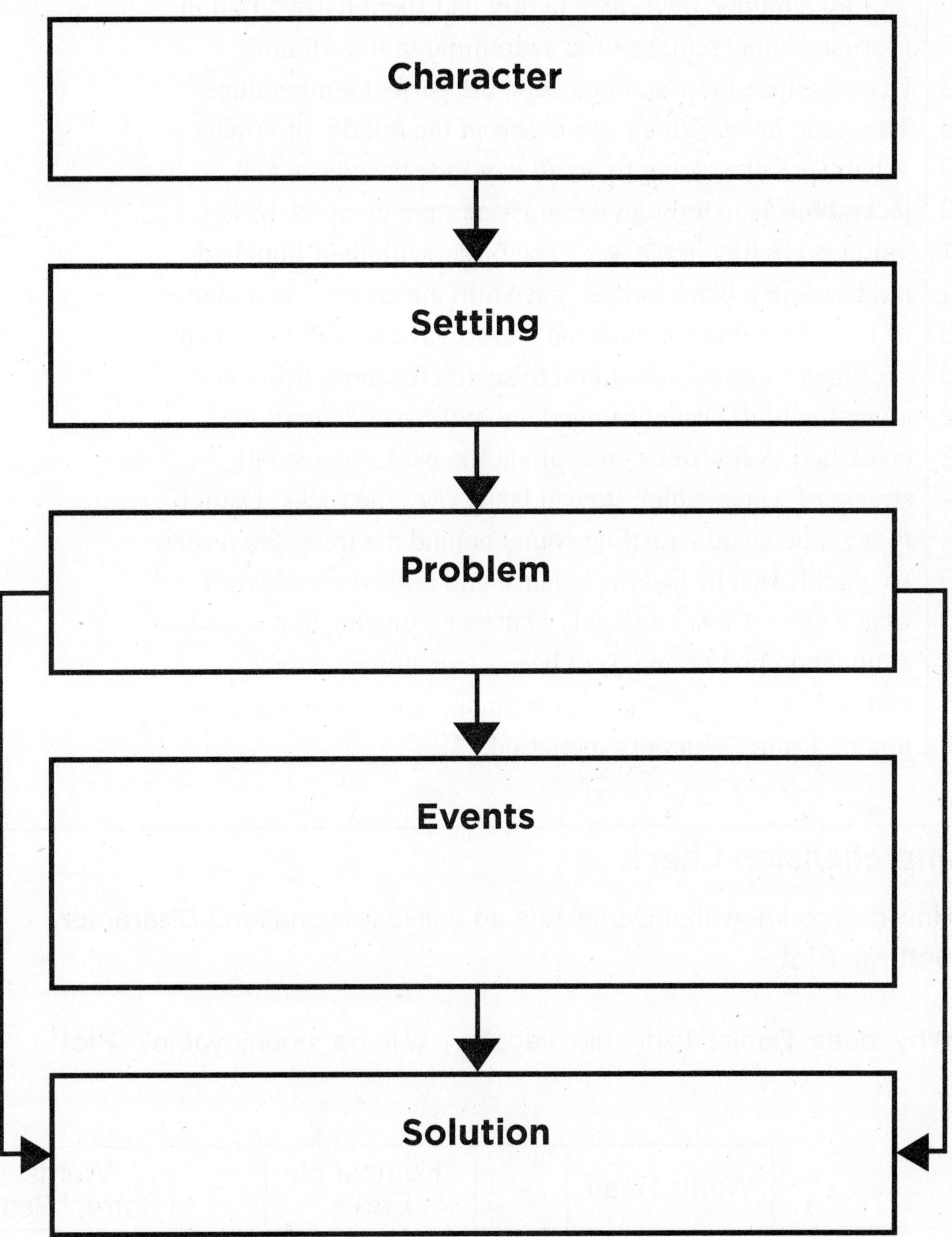

How does the information you wrote in this Story Map help you monitor comprehension of *The Summer of the Swans*?

At Home: Have the student use the map to retell the story.

Name ____

As I read, I will pay attention to pauses and stops.

Last summer, the Lopez family had spent its vacation in
10 Florida. Daniel remembered swimming in the Atlantic
17 Ocean, where the water had been the perfect temperature.
26 This year, he was stuck in a desert in the middle of nowhere.
39 What were they going to do all day long besides watch
50 jackrabbits leap through the grass or stare up at the turkey
61 vultures circling in the sky? The birds, with their hunched
71 red heads and black bodies, gave him the creeps. As a matter
83 of fact, the entire Chihuahuan Desert gave Daniel the creeps.
93 When Suzanne asked him to search for more firewood
102 along the trail, Daniel trudged down the path toward the
112 creek bed. A few trees grew along the banks of a small
124 stream of water, which flowed lazily over the rocks. Daniel
134 thought he heard a rustling sound behind the trees. He turned
145 so quickly that he lost his balance and fell over backward.
156 That's great, Daniel thought, whatever's making that sound—
164 a mountain lion or maybe a bear—can attack me. He
175 reached for a rock to use as a weapon. As the rustling grew
188 louder, Daniel's **anxiety** increased. 192

Comprehension Check

1. How do you know that Daniel has an active imagination? **Character, Setting, Plot**

2. Why does Daniel think his vacation will be unenjoyable? **Plot**

	Words Read	–	Number of Errors	=	Words Correct Score
First Read		–		=	
Second Read		–		=	

At Home: Help the student read the passage, paying attention to the goal at the top of the page

Name ______________________________

Write a title and a caption that make sense with the following picture. Your caption should answer the questions: *who, what, when, where,* and *how.* Remember to include names and dates and to use your observational skills to come up with as many specific details as possible.

____

____

____

____

____

____

____

____

____

At Home: Together, discuss how photographs and caption lines help readers better understand newspaper articles.

Name ______________________________

In a dictionary, the multiple-meaning word *run* has many definitions. *Run* is listed as a noun, a verb, and as part of a verb phrase. Write your own dictionary definitions for *run* that include each part of speech. Show definitions for at least ten meanings of the word with an example phrase or sentence for each definition.

1. ______________________________
____

2. ______________________________

3. ______________________________

4. ______________________________

5. ______________________________

6. ______________________________
____

7. ______________________________

8. ______________________________
____

9. ______________________________
____

10. ______________________________

At Home: With family members, brainstorm other meanings for the word *run*. See how many meanings each person can find.

Name ____

Sort the words by short vowel sound and by the variant spelling of that sound. Then write the vowel sound, spellings, and words in the charts below.

again	cassette	done	gazelle	pretty
sweat	against	cayenne	double	glove
money	rhythm	shove	thread	analysis
cylinder	edge	head	month	rough
some	tough	damage	enough	love
myth	said	son	witness	beverage
dead	front	lynx	Paulette	spread

Sound	Other Spellings			
short e	**e**	**ea**	**ai**	**eCCe**
short i	**i**	**y**	**e**	**aCe**
short u	**o**	**ou**	**oCe**	

At Home: Together, brainstorm other words with variant spellings for these short vowel sounds. Then write them under the heading "Other Spellings" in the chart.

Name ____

Use the words in the box to finish each analogy.

remote	withstood	venomous	vegetation
undergrowth	interpreter	escort	foretold

In an analogy the symbol : means "is to" and the symbol :: means "as."
A : B :: C : D means "A is to B as C is to D."

1. attorney : lawyer :: translator : ____________________

2. urban : rural :: public : ____________________

3. observer : watcher :: chaperone : ____________________

4. overtook : passed :: predicted : ____________________

5. gazette : newspaper :: foliage : ____________________

6. canopy : overhang :: shrub : ____________________

7. tender : rough :: healthful : ____________________

8. abandoned : remained :: submitted : ____________________

Now write two analogies of your own. Each analogy should include a vocabulary word from the box above.

9. ________________:________________::________________:________________

10. ________________:________________::________________:________________

Name ______________________________

Plan a story about a city that is "lost." Fill in the chart to organize your ideas for the story. Your conclusion should end before the city is found.

Story Title: ______________________________

Character	
Main Character	
Character Traits	
Setting	
When	
Where	
Plot	
Problem	
Solution	
Conclusion	

Use the information in your chart to write the first paragraph of your story.

____

____

____

At Home: Together, discuss other lost cities you know or have heard about.

Name ______________________________

As you read *Lost City,* fill in the Character, Setting, Plot Chart.

Character	Setting	Plot

How does the information you wrote in this Character, Setting, Plot Chart help you analyze the story structure of *Lost City*?

At Home: Have the student use the chart to retell the story.

Name ____________________

As I read, I will pay attention to the pronunciation of names, pauses, and intonation.

Ouray (oo-RAY) veered off the trail and scrambled down the steep
11 side of the cliff. There wasn't much **vegetation** in his way, only a
24 scattering of pinyon pines and cactus. Soon the boy was sitting on a
37 sandstone ledge and looking down into a deep pool of icy, blue water.
50 An underground spring gushed through the rocks and kept the water cold
62 even on the hottest days. In the summer, Ouray loved imagining he was
75 a red-tailed hawk about to seize his prey. He would leap off the ledge
89 with his arms outstretched and swoop headfirst into the cool water
100 beneath him.

102 But now it was still early in the spring, and Ouray had something else
116 on his mind besides swimming. He untangled a long line of leather
128 strands that were knotted together and then weighted one end with a
140 round piece of lead. Next Ouray attached a small barbed bone and
152 concealed it under a few shiny feathers. He was ready.

162 Ouray threw out his fishing line and heard it hit the surface of the
176 pond with a perfect plunk. There was nothing left for him to do but
190 dangle his legs over the side of the sandstone ledge and wait for a big, fat
206 trout to strike. 209

Comprehension Check

1. How do you know that Ouray likes to daydream **Character, Setting, Plot**

2. What clues tell you that this story takes place in the Southwest? **Setting**

	Words Read	–	Number of Errors	=	Words Correct Score
First Read		–		=	
Second Read		–		=	

At Home: Help the student read the passage, paying attention to the goal at the top of the page.

Name ______________________________

Plan a social studies textbook article about *The Lost Neighborhood.* Think about your neighborhood and how it would look 200 years in the future. What would future archaeologists infer about your neighborhood? What mysterious artifacts might scientists find? Use facts about your neighborhood and research strategies from *The Lost City* to plan your article. For your article show the following:

- a heading for that section of the text
- a brief description of the purpose of the text

At Home: Together, discuss what parts of your neighborhood will probably exist 200 years from now.

Name ______________________________

Write 20 compound words using the words in the box below. Organize the words in a chart according to the type of compound each one is—closed, open, or hyphenated.

down	drive	fire	home	ice
in	line	make	run	side
skate	truck	up	way	work

Closed	Open	Hyphenated

Choose two of the compound words you made and write a definition of each based on its word parts.

1. ______________________________

____

2. ______________________________

____

____

At Home: With other family members, take turns making up definitions for the compound words in the chart and challenging others to guess the meaning of the words.

Name ______________________________

Write as many rhyming words as you can for each word given. List the rhyming words in the correct columns according to the spelling of the long vowel sound.

1. creek	***ee* (long *e*)**	***ea* (long *e*)**	**Other Spellings**
2. wait	***ai* (long *a*)**	***a_e* (long *a*)**	**Other Spellings**
3. goal	***oa* (long *o*)**	***o_e* (long *o*)**	**Other Spellings**
4. cry	***y* (long *i*)**		

At Home: Together, make up some rhymes, using words from the lists you made.

Name ________________________________

Fill in the blanks with a vocabulary word from the box to create a multiple-choice test. Then circle the correct answer.

absorb	altered	concentrated	erode	innovations

1. Which of these is a synonym for ______________?

a. wash away slowly **c.** help out

b. increase **d.** bite into

2. Which of these is an antonym for ______________?

a. strengthened **c.** diluted

b. condensed **d.** boiled down

3. Which of these is the meaning of ______________?

a. to take in **c.** to leave alone

b. to squeeze out **d.** to forgive

4. Which word means "______________?"

a. fixed **c.** removed

b. changed **d.** built

5. Television, cell phones, and computers are twentieth century ______________.

a. inhabitants **c.** inoculations

b. innocents **d.** inventions

One way to keep track of the **main ideas** and **details** in a long selection is to make an outline. An outline provides key information in a concise way.

Make an outline for the following essay. Use Roman numerals for main ideas. Use letters for supporting details.

Moths and butterflies have unusual feeding habits. Did you know that some moths do not have mouths and only eat when they are in the caterpillar stage? These moths live off stored energy their entire adult lives. Also, many butterflies and moths can taste food through the hairlike structures on their feet.

Moths and butterflies that stay in cold climates for the winter have special chemicals similar to antifreeze inside their bodies that help protect them from the cold. Other moths and butterflies migrate to warmer climates such as California or Mexico.

I. ______________________________

A. ______________________________

____

B. ______________________________

____

II. ______________________________

____

A. ______________________________

____

B. ______________________________

____

At Home: Ask the student to use the outline to summarize the essay about moths and butterflies.

Name ______________________________

As you read *Gecko Glue, Cockroach Scouts, and Spider Silk Bridges*, fill in the Main Idea Web.

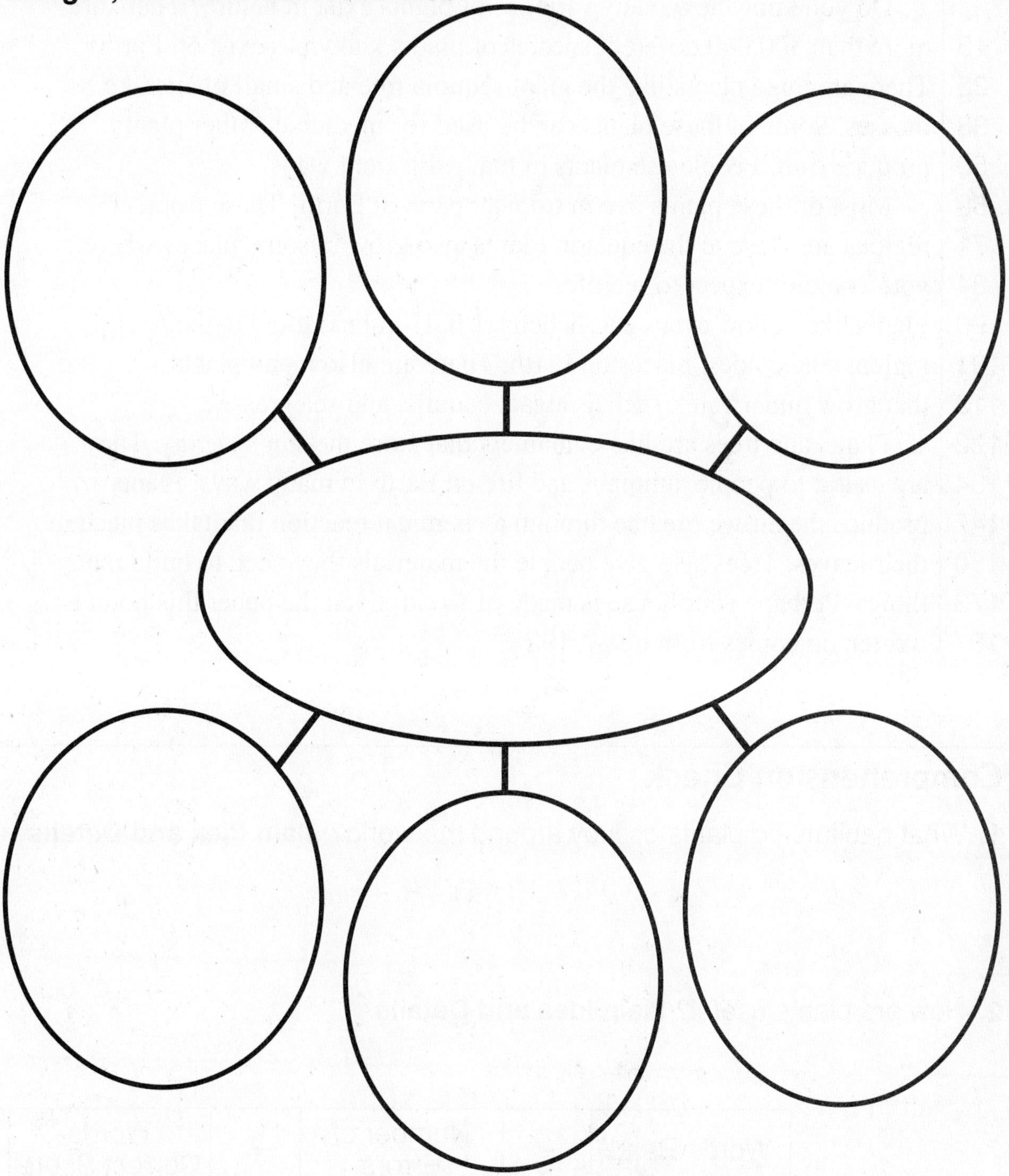

How does the information you wrote in this Main Idea Web help you make inferences and analyze the story structure of *Gecko Glue, Cockroach Scouts, and Spider Silk Bridges*?

At Home: Have the student use the chart to retell the story.

Name ______________________________

As I read, I will pay attention to the pronunciation of difficult words.

Do you know how many varieties of plants exist in nature? There are
13 more than 300,000 different species of plants known to exist on Earth!
25 There are huge plants like the giant sequoia tree and small plants like
38 mosses. Some of these plants can be used for medicine. Other plants
50 produce fruit. People use plants in many different ways.
59 Most of these plants live in tropical parts of Earth! These tropical
71 regions are close to the equator. Plants also grow in some places where
84 you wouldn't expect to see life.
90 Plants like yellow avens and lichens (LIGH-kuhns) grow in the Arctic
101 regions, the coldest places on Earth. There are also many plants
112 that grow underwater, such as algae, cattails, and sea grasses.
122 Plants and trees are like containers that store the sun's energy. They
134 are useful to people, animals, and life on Earth in many ways. Plants
147 produce the air we breathe through a chemical reaction that takes place in
160 their leaves. Trees also give people the materials they need to build many
173 things. Perhaps your house is made of wood. Even the paper this book is
187 written on comes from trees. 192

Comprehension Check

1. What habitats do plants occupy around the world? **Main Idea and Details**

2. How are plants useful? **Main Idea and Details**

	Words Read	–	Number of Errors	=	Words Correct Score
First Read		–		=	
Second Read		–		=	

At Home: Help the student read the passage, paying attention to the goal at the top of the page.

Name ______________________________

You are going to write a report about geckos for your science class. You go to the library and search the electronic card catalog for the subject "gecko." The entries below show the results of your search.

Explain why you would or would not use each book to do the research for your report.

1. 639.3 CHU Chung, Jesse, Geckos: Everything You Need to Know About Caring for Geckos; with color photos by Jesse Chung and illustrations by Bonnie Smith
New York, NY: Priceless Press, 2001
A complete pet-owner's guide

____

____

2. J 639.3 TEL Tellman, Grace, A Picture Dictionary of Lizards
New York, NY: Children's Publishers, 2004
Iguana, chameleon, gecko, anole, lizard.

____

____

3. J FIC GEM Gem, Jim, Gumshoe Gecko and the Missing Parrot
Los Angeles, CA: Reader's Inc., 2002
Gecko-Fiction, Mysteries–Fiction, Humor–Fiction

____

____

4. 639.3 SMI Smith, Janell, Raising Leopard Geckos
Chicago, IL: Homestead Co., 2005
Geckos, Leopard, A Guide to Raising

____

____

____

At Home: Discuss with the student where in the local library he or she would locate resources when doing research for a school project.

Name ________________________________

Specialized vocabulary words are words used for a specific area, such as science. Write a paragraph that includes these words with definitions as context clues to help your reader understand the word's meanings.

bacteria *n. pl.* single-celled microorganisms

biological *adj.* of, or relating to life and the processes of life

chemical *adj.* of, relating to, or produced by chemistry or chemistry processes

gene *n.* the part of a chromosome that determines which characteristics an organism inherits and how those characteristics develop

organism *n.* a living being made up of organs separate in function, but mutually dependent ________________________________

____

____

____

____

____

____

____

____

____

____

____

____

At Home: Discuss specialized vocabulary used by teachers, doctors, police officers, or people in other fields of work.

Name ___________________________

For each word given write two rhyming words with the dipthongs *ei* or *ie* that stand for long *e* or long *a*.

1. receive ____________ ____________

2. neigh ____________ ____________

3. eight ____________ ____________

4. brief ____________ ____________

5. field ____________ ____________

Write the opening paragraph of a story about a scientist. In your story, use at least five words with *ei* or *ie* spellings that stand for long *e* or long *a*.

At Home: Together, write as many words in which *ei* or *ie* stand for the long *e* or long *a* sounds as you can in one minute.

Name ______________________________

Write a short story using the vocabulary words that are in the box. Underline each vocabulary word that you use.

chameleon	rummaged	generosity	scrounging
pathetic	undetected	ricocheting	

Name ______________________________

A ***cause*** is the reason an event happens. An ***effect*** is what happens as a result. In some stories, each event causes another to happen. Organize each of the following statements into cause-and-effect relationships using the chart below.

- The rope from the trap tightened around Brother Rabbit's ankle and he was hoisted up into the air.
- Brother Rabbit told the wolf that he would teach him to catch hundreds of rabbits each day if the wolf would set him free.
- Greedy Wolf rushed to the trap to eat the rabbit.
- This is why wolves and rabbits are not friends to this day.
- Brother Rabbit was walking but he looked up to see what had made the noise, so he stopped looking at the ground and stepped into a trap.

Cause	Effect
Brother Rabbit was walking when he heard a strange sound in the trees.	
	Brother Rabbit cried out loudly in alarm.
Greedy Wolf heard Rabbit's cry.	
	Greedy Wolf set Brother Rabbit free.
Brother Rabbit ran away to safety.	

At Home: Together, talk about events in newspapers or magazines where you can identify causes and effects.

Name ______________________________

As you read *The Magic Gourd,* fill in the Cause and Effect Chart.

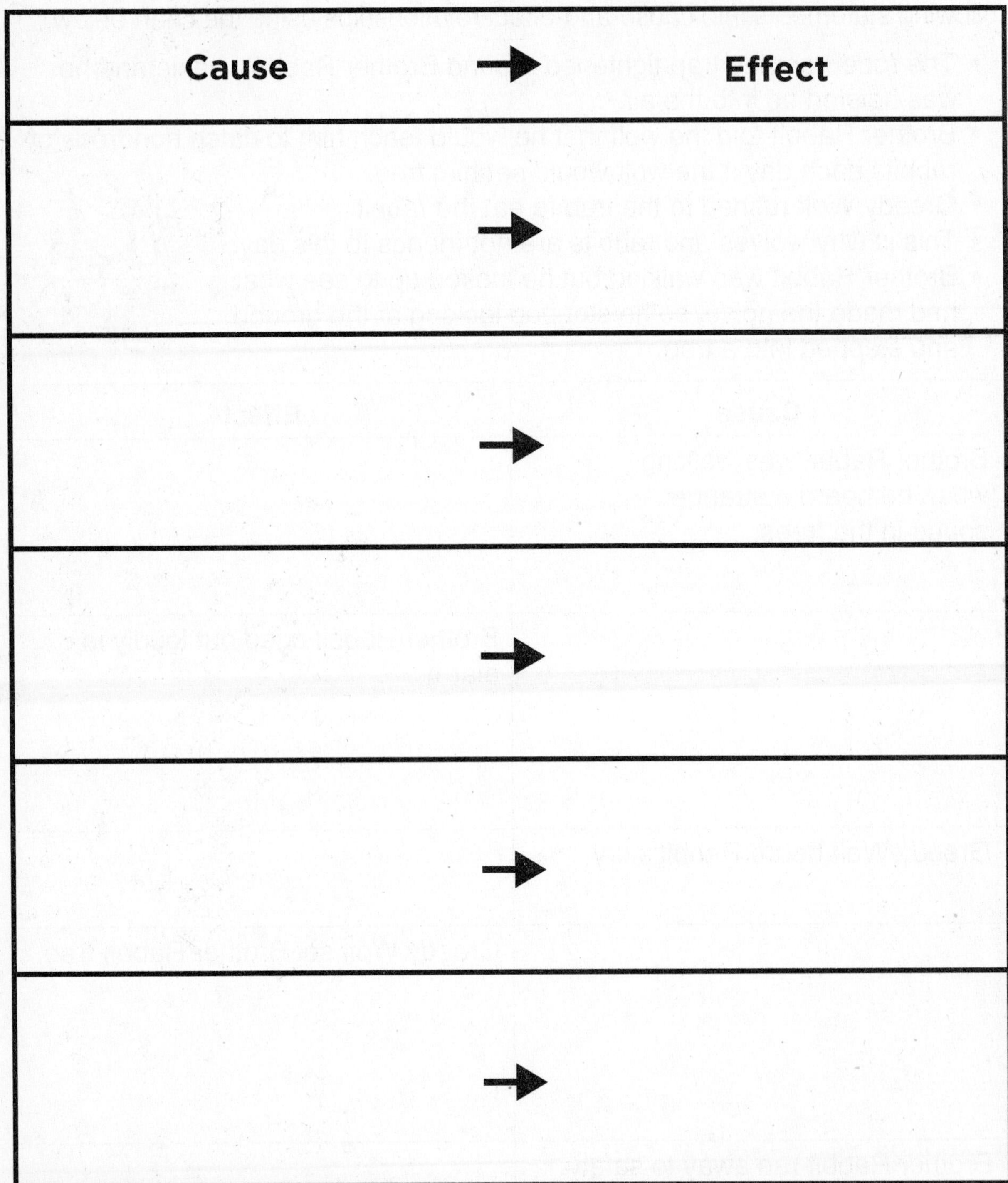

Cause	→	Effect
	→	
	→	
	→	
	→	
	→	

How does the information you wrote in this Cause and Effect Chart help you make inferences and analyze the story structure of *The Magic Gourd*?

At Home: Have the student use the chart to retell the story.

Name ______________________________

As I read, I will pay attention to punctuation.

Dance has been an important art form since ancient times. People
11 wrote music to accompany dance. They designed masks and costumes to
22 better express their dances. Dances were a way for people to tell stories.
35 Words were not necessary.
39 Why do people dance? People in some cultures have used dance as a
52 ritual. They might have danced to end a drought that caused a **famine**.
65 Other dances celebrated the harvest. Some traditional dances hoped to
75 cure or heal someone.
79 Add costumes, music, and masks to a dance and you have more than
97 just movement; you also have a story. Today many dances are performed
109 for entertainment. Ballets often retell fairy tales. Modern dances might
119 retell a myth or demonstrate a feeling. All dances show the
130 dancer's artistry.
132 No matter where you travel in the world, you will almost always find
145 dance. Dances might be traditional and part of a festival or modern with
158 people moving in time to their favorite music. Dance is an art form that
172 people continue to use to express themselves. 179

Comprehension Check

1. Why might people perform rituals? What effect do they hope to receive? **Cause and Effect**

2. How do people express themselves in dance? **Character**

	Words Read	–	Number of Errors	=	Words Correct Score
First Read		–		=	
Second Read		–		=	

At Home: Help the student read the passage, paying attention to the goal at the top of the page.

Name ____________________

A time line uses intervals to show events over time. When a time span is great and space is limited, the time line is sometimes compressed.

Read the time line below. Use it to write a paragraph about the history of Mali under its great ruler Mansa Musa.

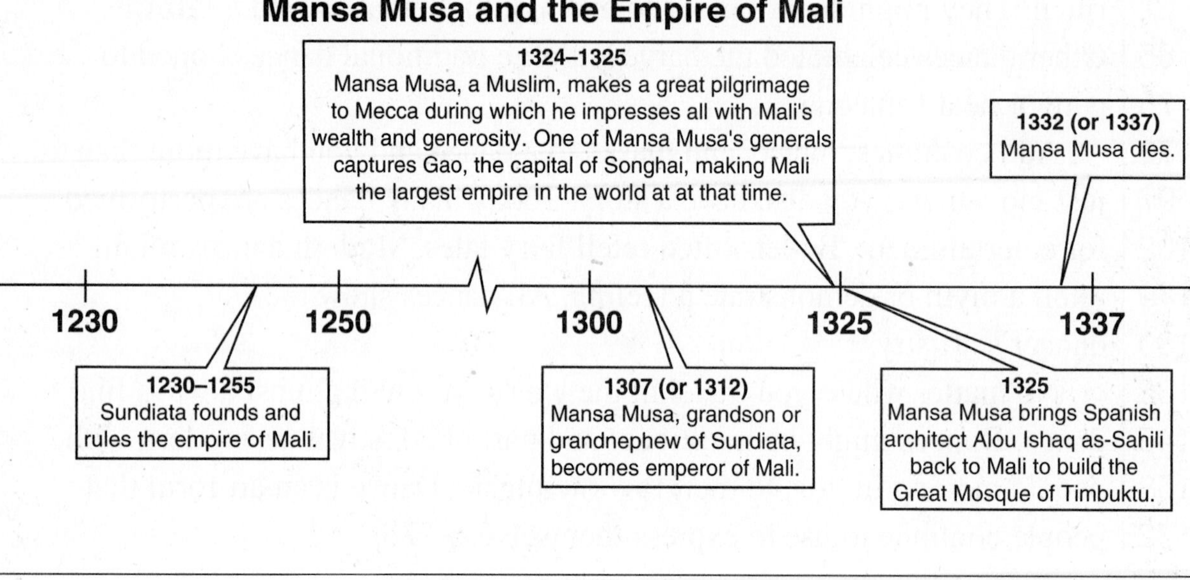

____

____

____

____

____

____

____

____

____

____

____

At Home: Together make a time line of key events that have happened in your household over the past 10 years.

Name ______________________________

Read the meanings of these words that describe the land, the plants, and the animals of Mali. Then use each word in a sentence, followed by a restatement that makes the meaning of the word clear.

1. acacia: a shrub with small flowers and leaves that often has thorns near the base of its stalks ______________________________

____

____

2. baobab: a tree native to Africa that can grow to be 30 feet in diameter and 60 feet high. The trunk is barrel-like and can be carved out to collect water or to act as a shelter. ______________________________

____

____

3. ostrich: a flightless bird native to Africa. At about 8 feet tall with a weight of about 345 pounds, it is the largest living bird species in the world. ________

____

____

4. savanna: a plain of tall grass with widely spaced trees that exists in a hot, dry climate ______________________________

____

____

At Home: Take turns using a vocabulary word in a sentence. Then follow that sentence with a restatement that contains a definition.

Name ____________________

An anagram is a word whose letters are rearranged to make another word. For example, *rail* is an anagram for *lair.*

The clues for this crossword puzzle are anagrams for words with *r*-controlled vowels. Complete the puzzle by writing the *r*-controlled words in the boxes. Three words have been done for you.

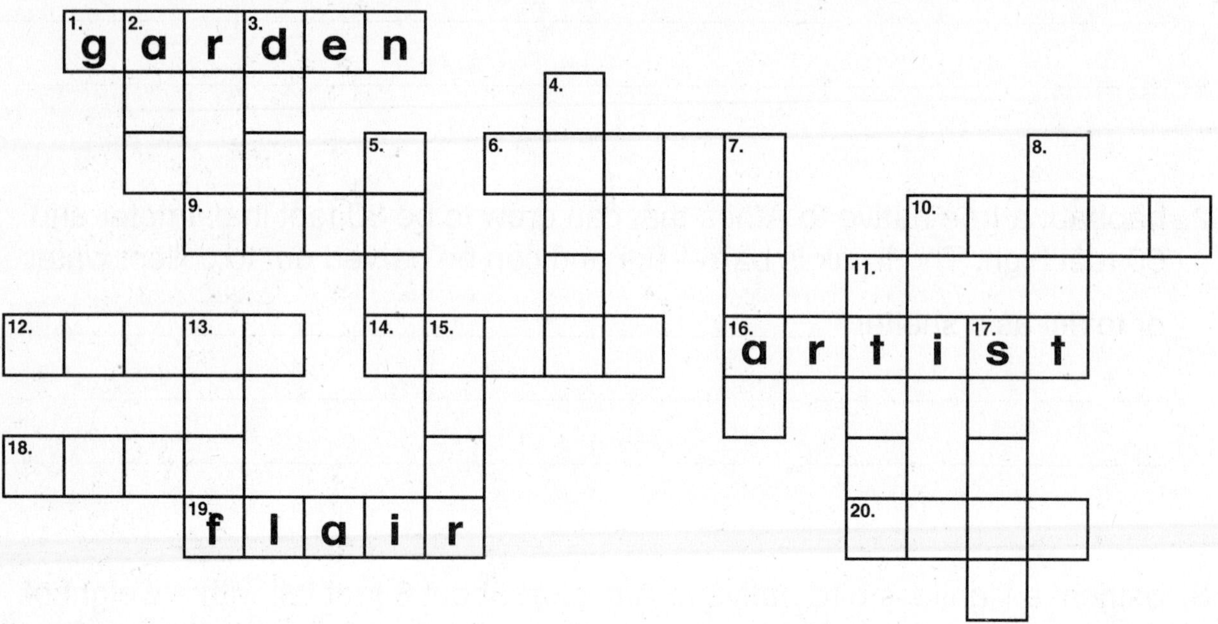

Across		**Down**	
1. gander	**14.** shore	**2.** mar	**8.** rots
6. scorn	**16.** traits	**3.** read	**11.** rates
9. reap	**18.** rate	**4.** sport	**13.** furs
10. north	**19.** frail	**5.** char	**15.** door
12. harms	**20.** near	**7.** wears	**17.** parks

At Home: Name some words that contain *r*-controlled vowels and ask the student to find anagrams for those words.

Name ______________________

analyzing	conserve	dehydrated	embedded
propelled	sedated	speculated	vital

Many people work to save endangered animals. Write a fictional television news report about the rescue of an endangered animal. Use each vocabulary word at least once in your news piece and underline the word.

Name ______________________________

Read the following details. Then write an essay using three of the details. When you are finished, underline the main idea with two lines and underline three supporting facts with one line.

Details:

1. The Sumatran tiger is one of only five subspecies that still exist.
2. They are native to the Indonesian island of Sumatra, where about 400 still remain. Only about 610 are thought to exist worldwide.
3. The tiger population is thought to have fallen by about 95% since the beginning of the twentieth century.
4. Tigers hunt their prey, but they are successful only one or two times out of every 20 attempts. They prefer to eat wild deer and wild pigs, and can eat up to 80 pounds of meat in one sitting.
5. Loss of habitat, illegal hunting of tigers and their prey, and an expanding human population continue to threaten the Sumatran tiger's survival.
6. Sumatran tigers can weigh up to 500 pounds and measure more than nine feet long from the nose to the tip of the tail. They are characterized by their gold-and-black striped fur and blue eyes.

____

____

____

____

____

____

____

____

____

____

____

____

At Home: Talk about other endangered species that you know of and what you might be able to do to help.

Name ______________________________

As you read *Interrupted Journey,* fill in the Main Idea Web.

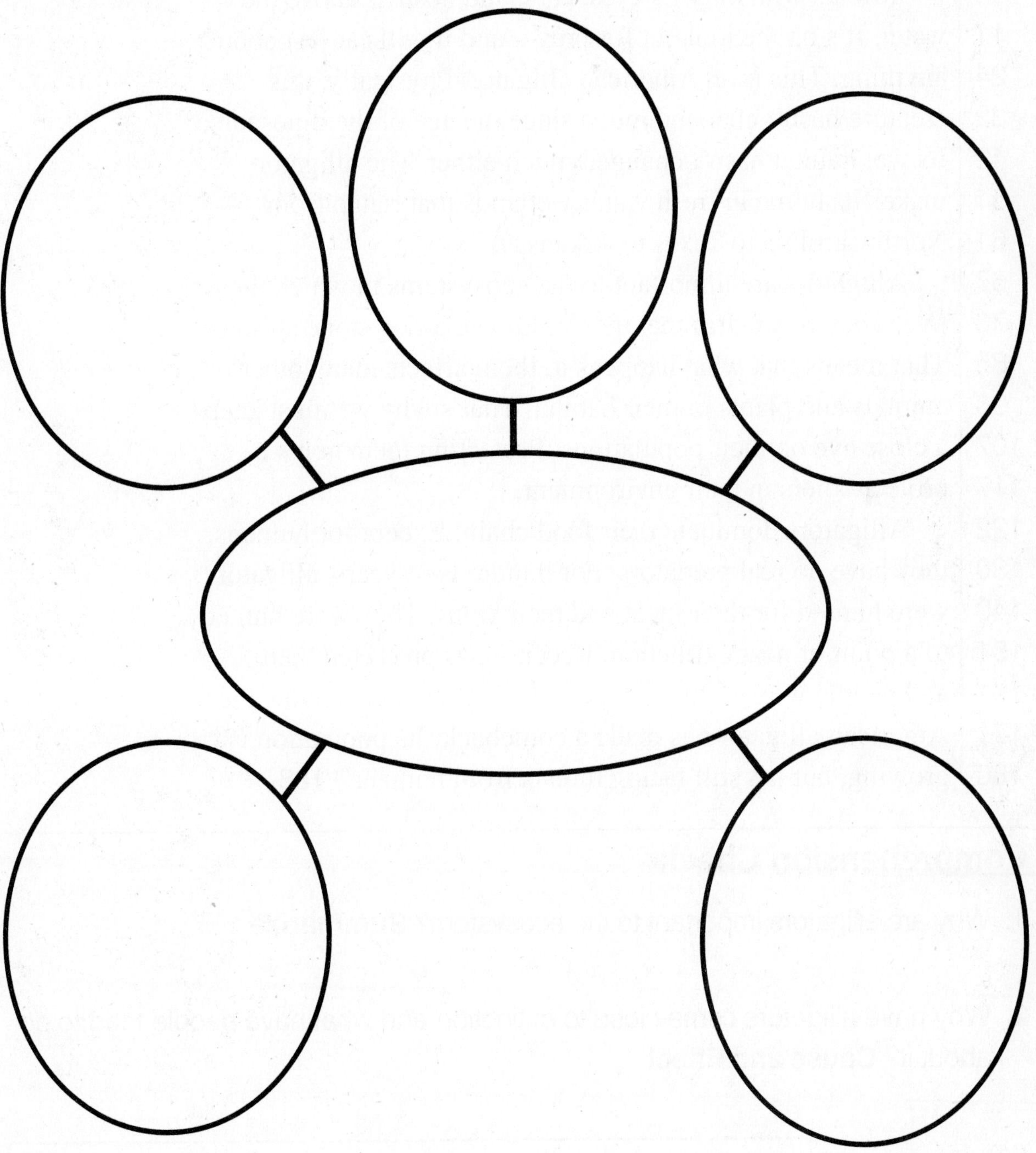

How does the information you wrote in this Main Idea Web help you make inferences and analyze the story structure of *Interrupted Journey*?

At Home: Have the student use the chart to retell the story.

Name ______________________________

As I read, I will pay attention to tempo.

It floats with only its eyes, ears, and nostrils above the
11 water. It's on the lookout for prey—and it will eat just about
24 anything. This is an American alligator. Physically, this
32 creature hasn't changed much since the age of the dinosaurs.
42 Its wet habitat hasn't changed much either. The alligator
51 makes its home in fresh water wetlands that range from
61 North Carolina to Texas to Arkansas.
67 Alligators are important to the ecosystems in which they
76 live. They're so **vital** that they're known as keystone species.
86 That means that what happens to them affects many other
96 animals and plants in their habitat. That's why we must keep
107 a close eye on their populations. Protecting them helps us
117 protect others in their environment.
122 Alligators dominate their food chain. Except for humans,
130 they have no real predators. For hundreds of years, alligators
140 were hunted for their meat and their skins. They were hunted
151 to a point of near extinction. Recent laws protected them,
161 and people worked to save these ancient creatures. Now the
171 American alligator has made a comeback. Its population is
180 growing, but it's still facing threats from humans. 188

Comprehension Check

1. Why are alligators important to the ecosystem? **Summarize**

2. Why have alligators come close to extinction and what have people tried to do about it? **Cause and Effect**

	Words Read	–	Number of Errors	=	Words Correct Score
First Read		–		=	
Second Read		–		=	

At Home: Help the student read the passage paying attention to the goal at the top of the page.

Name ___________________________

Practice

Literary Element: Alliteration and Imagery

Write a free-verse poem about endangered animals. The words below can help you include alliteration and imagery in your verses.

sleek	brush	scent	fresh
whisper	sea	forest	earth
wind	watch	wish	breeze
sink	steal	wrestle	flashy
dawn	furry	sigh	startle
fleet	stare	fragrant	browse

____

____

____

____

____

____

____

____

____

Examine your poem. Describe the poetic elements that you chose to express your ideas.

____

____

____

____

____

____

At Home: Find examples of alliteration and imagery in a favorite poem.

Name ____

Write a word to complete each analogy. Use a dictionary or thesaurus if needed.

1. usual : rare :: customary : ____________________

2. confound : clarify :: confuse : ____________________

3. cling : abandon :: adhere : ____________________

4. preservation : loss :: recovery : ____________________

5. contribute : withhold :: cooperate : ____________________

6. instinct : reasoning :: impulse : ____________________

7. gradual : periodic :: continuous : ____________________

8. excitement : apathy :: energy : ____________________

9. hypothesis : proof :: theory : ____________________

10. crowd : person :: group : ____________________

Look at the analogies above. Describe the relationships you see among the four elements in each analogy, and then write a new analogy that fits the pattern.

____

____

____

____

At Home: Challenge the student to write some analogies that include antonyms and then to explain the relationships among the words.

Name ____________________

Read the compound words. Use a slash mark to separate the word into two smaller words. Then use a word in each set in a sentence.

1. penname lifeguard shoreline seaweed

___

2. pancake peanut applesauce buttercup

___

3. skateboard windshield streetcar wheelchair

___

4. toothbrush suitcase teacup wastebasket

___

___

5. turtleneck bathrobe hairbrush wristwatch

___

6. clubhouse homerun crosswalk drive-in

___

7. highrise skyscraper highway rainbow

___

___

8. waterfall raindrop downpour washcloth

___

___

At Home: Together, think of as many other compound words as you can.

Name ______________________________

A. Write the vocabulary word from the box that is an antonym of the given word. Then write a sentence that includes both the vocabulary word and its antonym.

absorb	altered	anxiety	generosity	remote

1. unchanged ______________ ______________________________
____

2. nearby ______________ ______________________________
____

3. stinginess ______________ ______________________________
____
____

4. calm ______________ ______________________________
____
____

5. reflect ______________ ______________________________
____

B. Write a definition for each vocabulary word.

6. dehydrated ______________________________________
7. foretold ______________________________________
8. speculated ______________________________________
9. ricocheting ______________________________________
10. engulf ______________________________________

At Home: Have the student use the vocabulary words in Part B in sentences.

Name ______________________________

A. Choose a vocabulary word from the box to complete each sentence in the paragraph. Write your answer on the line provided.

chameleon	concentrated	pathetic	rummaged	undetected

I ________________ through the refrigerator looking for something to feed my new pet ________________. The refrigerator was almost empty. It was sadly ________________! There were a few eggs, a can of ________________ orange juice, and an apple. I was about to close the refrigerator door, when I spotted something that had gone ________________ in the bottom drawer—lettuce! My pet will like that.

B. Write a context clue or synonym for each underlined vocabulary word.

6. A <u>cascade</u> of water created a temporary ________________.

7. Wind and rain <u>erode</u> and ________________ away rocks and even mountains.

8. His prescription was <u>vital</u>, so he programmed his computer to remind him about the ________________ errand.

9. Near the finish line, one runner <u>propelled</u> himself forward and ________________ past the other front runners to win the race.

10. After I spent my allowance, I found myself in the embarrassing situation of <u>scrounging</u> and ________________ money from older brother.

At Home: Make up more sentences using vocabulary words and make up context clues for the words.

Write clues for each vocabulary word in the crossword puzzle.

Charlie's Boys

Crossword puzzle words:

- 1 Down: pennant
- 2 Down: resemblance
- 3 Across: embarrassment
- 4 Down: regulation
- 5 Down: grouchy
- 6 Across: postmarked
- 7 Across: enthralled
- 8 Across: inscribed

Across

3. ______________________

6. ______________________

7. ______________________
____

8. ______________________

Down

1. ______________________

2. ______________________

4. ______________________

5. ______________________

Name ________________________________

A scout for the varsity softball team made these notes about a player on the junior varsity team.

Use these notes to make inferences about the player's strengths and weaknesses. Then write the assessment and recommendation parts of the report.

Scouting Report

Player: Jenny Levins | Grade: 6 | Age: 12 | Date: April 3
Position(s): Pitcher | Team: Kennedy JV

Offense: Batting and Base Running
1. 5 at bats: 1 home run, 2 doubles, 1 strikeout
2. running speed: average for age; not afraid to slide
3. clutch hitter, hit home run to break tie and win game

Defense: Position Play and Fielding
1. good mechanics on most pitches
2. pitches a variety of balls; ball placement developing
3. good reaction time, knows which base to cover

Mental Game
1. leader; other players look to her.
2. positive attitude; shakes off bad pitches quickly
3. keeps play moving and works well with catcher

Overall Assessment

____

____

____

____

Recommendation

____

____

At Home: Together, discuss the qualities that a good team player possesses and give examples.

Name ______________________________

As you read *How Tía Lola Came to ~~Visit~~/Stay*, fill in the inferences Chart.

Text Clues and Prior Knowledge	Inferences

How does the information you wrote in this inferences chart help you make inferences about *How Tía Lola Came to ~~Visit~~/Stay*?

At Home: Have the student use the chart to retell the story.

Name ____________________________

As I read I will pay attention to pauses, stops, and intonation.

Tyrone joins the crush of students in the hallway. He heads for his locker,
14 where he expects to meet his closest friend, Malik. Tyrone and Malik have
27 grown up together in the same Philadelphia neighborhood. They've always
37 gone to the same schools, shared a love of sports, and told each other all
52 their problems and dreams. To Tyrone, who is an only child, Malik is like
66 the brother he never had.
71 As always, Malik is already at his locker right next to Tyrone's. Malik
84 never walks anywhere—he runs.
89 "Hey, man, how's it going?" Tyrone asks as he walks up to the locker.
103 "Same as usual," Malik answers. He asks Tyrone if he's still coming over
116 for the big game that night. Monday Night Football is featuring their home
129 team, the Philadelphia Eagles.
133 Malik dumps his books into his locker. This is our first year in middle
147 school, and Malik still hasn't changed, Tyrone thinks to himself. Malik has
159 never been much for homework.
164 "I have to double-check with my mom, but she already said it's okay
177 since it's a special occasion," answers Tyrone. 184

Comprehension Check

1. How do you know that Tyrone is responsible? **Make Inferences**

2. Why did the boys become friends? What effect has the friendship had on Tyrone? **Cause and Effect**

	Words Read	–	Number of Errors	=	Words Correct Score
First Read		–		=	
Second Read		–		=	

At Home: Help the student read the passage, paying attention to the goal at the top of the page

Practice

Name ____________________

Text Feature: Almanacs

In 2004, the Boston Red Sox of the American League won its first World Series championship since 1918. Use this index from a sports almanac to find information for a report on this historic event. Choose five entries that would be the most helpful in your research and give a reason for each choice.

Baseball
2004 World Series
2004 Year in Baseball
All-Star Game 2004
All-Time World Series Leaders
American League Championship Series 2004
American League Leaders 2004
American League Statistics 2004
Final Major League Standings 2004
Home Attendance 2004
Home-Run Leaders 1900–2004
Individual Batting Leaders 1900–2004
National League Championship Series 2004
National League Leaders 2004
Reverse the Curse: The Red Sox Win!
Runs Batted in 1900–2004
Stolen Bases 1900–2004
Team Batting Records 2004
Team Pitching Records 2004
World Series Winners 1903–2004

Entry 1: ____________________

Reason: ____________________

____

Entry 2: ____________________

Reason: ____________________

____

Entry 3: ____________________

Reason: ____________________

Entry 4: ____________________

Reason: ____________________

____

Entry 5: ____________________

Reason: ____________________

____

At Home: Choose a topic that everyone is familiar with such as baseball, and make up trivia questions to ask each other.

Name ______________________________

Add an inflectional ending from the box to each verb or adjective. Use the word with its inflectional ending in a sentence. Use each ending at least once.

Verb Endings	**Adjective Endings**
-s *-ed* *-ing*	*-er* *-est*

1. sprout ________ ________________________________

2. persist ________ ________________________________

3. gaze ________ ________________________________

4. grouchy ________ ________________________________

5. quaint ________ ________________________________

6. meek ________ ________________________________

7. strengthen ________ ________________________________

8. friendly ________ ________________________________

9. fluster ________ ________________________________

10. warm ________ ________________________________

At Home: Give the student a piece of junk mail or an old newspaper, and circle as many words with inflectional endings as he or she can find in one minute.

Name ____________________________

Use the plural form of as many words from the chart as you can as you write a story about someone who saves the day. Use the plural form of at least one word from each column. Underline the plural forms you use.

Column 1	Column 2	Column 3	Column 4
life	echo	piano	medium
half	hero	auto	bacterium
leaf	tomato	radio	curriculum
thief	volcano	solo	datum

At Home: Discuss the rule used to form the plurals of words in each column. Then brainstorm other words that fit each column's rules.

Name ____________________

Plan a game using vocabulary words. Write two clues for each vocabulary word. The game will be placed as follows.

If your partner can use your first clue to guess the vocabulary word you receive 2 points. If your partner can guess the word on the second clue you receive 1 point.

1. *spicy* for 2 points: ____________________
for 1 point: ____________________

2. *undone* for 2 points: ____________________
for 1 point: ____________________

3. *vigil* for 2 points: ____________________
for 1 point: ____________________

4. *ravaged* for 2 points: ____________________
for 1 point: ____________________

5. *marveled* for 2 points: ____________________
or 1 point: ____________________

6. *broadcast* for 2 points: ____________________
for 1 point: ____________________
____

7. *unsatisfactory* for 2 points: ____________________
for 1 point: ____________________

8. *calculations* for 2 points: ____________________
for 1 point: ____________________

Name ___________________________

The chart below shows facts about some planets. Make inferences from what you already know about the planets and the information given. Answer the questions.

Category	Mercury	Venus	Earth	Mars
Length of year	87.9 Earth days	224.7 Earth days	365.26 Earth days	686.98 Earth days
Length of day	58.6 Earth days	243 Earth days	23.93 hours	24.6 hours
Gravity	0.38 times that of Earth	0.91 times that of Earth	1.0 times that of Earth	0.38 times that of Earth

1. Your assignment is due tomorrow. On which planet would you like to be when you hear when your homework is due? Explain your inference.

____

____

____

2. Would you rather be older or younger than you are now? On which planet would you like to live so you could have the age you prefer? Explain.

____

____

3. You have a heavy backpack filled with books to carry home from school. On which planet would you prefer to be? Explain your inference.

____

____

At Home: Together, discuss other inferences that can be made from the information in the chart.

Name ___________________________________

As you read *The Night of the Pomegranate,* fill in the Inferences Diagram.

Evidence	Conclusion

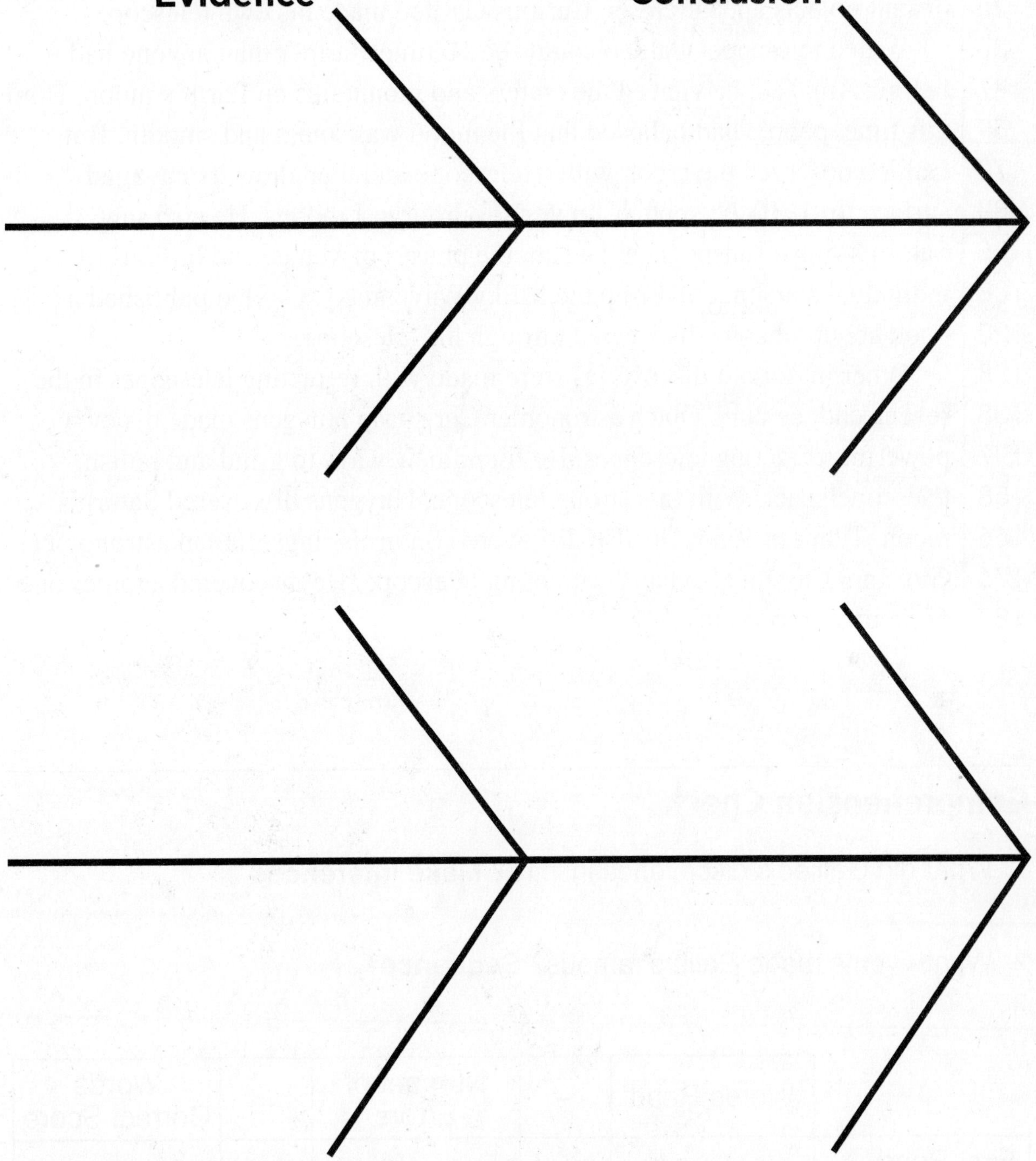

How does the information you wrote in this Inferences Diagram help you monitor comprehension of *The Night of the Pomegranate*?

At Home: Have the student use the chart to retell the story.

Name ____________________________________

As I read, I will pay attention to punctuation.

Italian astronomer Galileo Galilei was the first person to study the skies
12 with a telescope. In 1609, he heard about the tool in Holland that could make
26 distant objects appear closer. Curious Galileo made his own telescope.
36 With a telescope, Galileo could see 10 times farther than anyone had
47 before. Amazed, he viewed the craters and mountains on Earth's moon. Until
59 this time, people had believed that the moon was round and smooth. But
72 Galileo observed the moon with a telescope and then drew its **ravaged**
84 surface. In 1610, he spotted Jupiter's four largest moons. He also saw
95 Saturn's rings, sunspots on the sun, the phases of Venus, and billions of
108 individual stars that make up the Milky Way galaxy. Galileo published a
120 book about what he discovered through his telescope.
128 Other important discoveries were made with refracting telescopes in the
138 seventeenth century. Dutch astronomer Christiaan Huygens made his own
147 powerful refracting telescopes. He found new ways to grind and polish
158 telescopelenses. With this strong telescope, Huygens discovered Saturn's
166 moon, Titan, in 1655. He also discovered Saturn's rings. Italian astronomer
176 Giovanni Cassini also had a refracting telescope. He discovered another one
187 of Saturn's moons in 1672. 191

Comprehension Check

1. What did Galileo's discoveries inspire? **Make Inferences**

2. What events made Galileo famous? **Sequence**

	Words Read	–	Number of Errors	=	Words Correct Score
First Read		–		=	
Second Read		–		=	

At Home: Help the student read the passage, paying attention to the goal at the top of the page.

Name ______________________________

◆ Practice

Text Feature: Graphs

Use the information in the graph to write questions about the planets and their diameters. Write the answer as well.

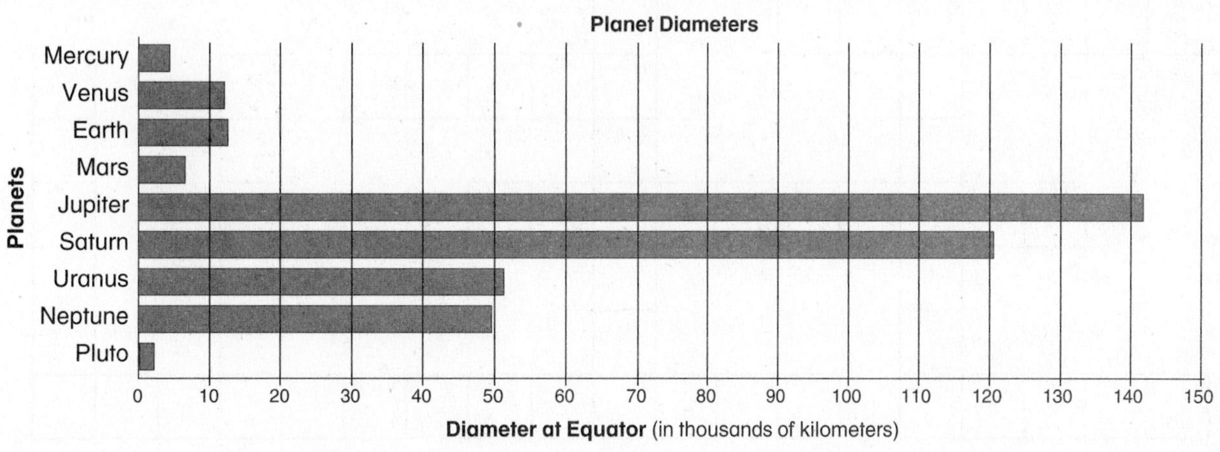

1. Question: ______________________________

____

Answer: ______________________________

2. Question: ______________________________

Answer: ______________________________

3. Question: ______________________________

____

Answer: ______________________________

4. Question: ______________________________

____

Answer: ______________________________

At Home: Together, discuss the graph and brainstorm other questions that can be answered by using the data on the graph.

Name ____________________

Use the pronunciation key and the clues to complete the crossword puzzle. Use a dictionary if you need help spelling a word.

Across

1. i kwā´ tər

4. ôr´ bit

7. bə nok´ yə lərs

8. spās

9. kon´ stə lā´ shən

10. gal´ ək sē

Down

2. twing´ kəl

3. rō´ tāts

5. plan´ it

6. ə stron´ ə mē

At Home: Explain how to use the pronunciation key to pronounce words from the puzzle clues. Use a dictionary to help.

Name ______________________________

Use at least 10 of the words from the box in a science fiction story about people traveling through our solar system. Each word from the box that you use should have an *-ed* or an *-ing* inflectional ending. Check a dictionary if needed.

barrel	bother	control	filter	occur
offer	orbit	outfit	outwit	propel
reason	refer	regret	slow	transfer
grind	travel	utter	weather	trace

At Home: Ten of the words in the box above double the final consonant before adding the *-ed* or *-ing* ending. Together, identify those words.

Name ______________________

Read the following passage. Revise the writing to make it more interesting. Include the following vocabulary words in your revision.

calamities mitigate devastating evacuate administer

In 1992, Hurricane Andrew hit Florida. It had winds of up to 125 miles per hour. Gusts of wind hit 175 miles per hour. Many buildings were torn apart. Thousands of people lost their homes. Some people were living in shelters. The wind whipped up the water. Tides were as high as 16.9 feet. People had had to leave their homes to be safe.

FEMA workers came to help the people of Florida. FEMA is a government agency. It helps people when there is a problem like a hurricane. It took more than $27 billion to clean up after Hurricane Andrew. It was one of the most expensive weather problems in U.S. history.

Name ______________________________

A. Read the following fictional facts about Disaster Relief.

a. House fires are the most frequent reasons people turn to Disaster Relief.

b. Disaster Relief workers teach CPR, first aid, and swimming courses in communities.

c. Disaster Relief's blood drives provide 30% of all donated blood in the United States.

d. Disaster Relief provides assistance to American troops overseas.

e. Disaster Relief helps Americans affected by hurricanes, blizzards, volcanic eruptions, earthquakes, and floods.

f. International Disaster Relief workers brought aid to the survivors of the 2003 earthquake in Iran and the 2004 Indian Ocean tsunami.

g. Disaster Relief plans to eliminate pox fever by vaccinating 500 million children in Asia.

h. Disaster Relief publishes books on learning first aid, babysitting, and pet safety.

i. Disaster Relief flies American military families around the world to see their enlisted family member.

j. Disaster Relief works with communities to help make disaster plans.

B. Write two generalizations about this agency. Cite the letter(s) of the facts you used to form your generalization.

1. Generalization: ______________________________

____

Support: ______________________________

2. Generalization: ______________________________

____

Support: ______________________________

3. Generalization: ______________________________

____

Support: ______________________________

At Home: Together, discuss emergency aid organizations and their missions.

Name ______________________________

As you read *Zoo Story*, fill in the Generalizations Chart.

Important Information	Generalization

How does the information you wrote in this Generalizations Chart help you monitor comprehension of *Zoo Story*?

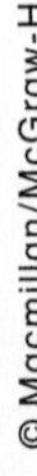

At Home: Have the student use the chart to retell the story.

Name ____________________

As I read, I will pay attention to the pronunciation of vocabulary and other difficult words.

The journey took eight days of walking through the desert. The
11 mother, father, and five children had nothing left when they arrived at
23 the relief camp. Once they had owned 50 goats and 20 cattle. But their
37 last cow had died. With no food or hope, the family had set out under the
53 hot sun to find help.
58 This was a common scene in Ethiopia (ee-thee-OH-pee-ah) in the year
69 2000. Ethiopia is a country in the Horn of Africa, the easternmost part of
83 the continent. It has a population of nearly 65 million people. In 2000
96 about ten million people faced terrible hunger and thirst. The country was
108 in the middle of one of the worst droughts it had ever suffered. Drought is
123 a weather pattern in which there is very little rainfall.
133 Drought is a fact of life in Ethiopia. Since the 1970s, Ethiopia has
146 had many years of severe drought. Ethiopia is a country of farmers and
159 animal herders. Its people rely on crops and livestock for food and
171 income. Very little rain means that crops fail and animals die. Droughts
183 also mean there is a shortage of water for drinking and cooking. The
196 people in Ethiopia needed help from other countries to take care of its
209 people during these **calamities**. 213

Comprehension Check

1. Why is life so difficult in rural Ethiopia? **Make Generalizations**

2. Why did the family risk crossing the desert? What was the result? **Cause and Effect**

	Words Read	–	Number of Errors	=	Words Correct Score
First Read		–		=	
Second Read		–		=	

At Home: Help the student read the passage, paying attention to the goal at the top of the page.

Name ______________________________

You have to do a science project on hurricanes. Explain how you might use the following Internet resources while preparing and writing your project. Also tell the key words you might use in your search and how you might modify your searches if needed.

- online resources, such as dictionaries and encyclopedias
- search engines
- databases

At Home: Use the Internet to research a subject of interest. Explain how to use online resources, search engines, and/or databases.

Name ___________________________

A. Read the following paragraphs. Think about how you could rewrite them, using context clues to make them clearer to the reader.

In the United States, **landslides** are responsible for about 2 billion dollars worth of damage each year. Many landslides are linked with heavy **precipitation** and quick **melting** of snow and ice.

During heavy precipitation, the soil on a steep slope becomes **saturated.** Eventually some of it begins to slip **downhill.** As the soil and rocks continue downhill, **friction** and the weight of the **debris** loosen more soil. Before long, there is an **avalanche.** Landslides can travel more than 35 miles per hour taking with them not only soil and rocks, but boulders, trees, and even cars. Landslides are **geologic hazards.** They occur in areas with steep **hillsides.**

B. Write context clues on the lines below that you could use for the boldface words in the paragraphs. Use a dictionary as needed.

1. ___________________________
____

2. ___________________________

3. ___________________________
____

4. ___________________________

5. ___________________________

6. ___________________________

7. ___________________________

8. ___________________________
____
____

9. ___________________________
____

10. ___________________________

At Home: Together, look through a textbook to find boldface terms. Then search for context clues that help explain the meaning of those terms.

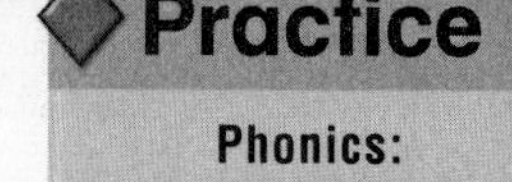

Name ____________________

Phonics: Variant and Ambiguous Vowels

Write at least five words that have the vowel sound of the underlined letters in each given word.

s<u>ou</u>ght	m<u>ou</u>nd	fo<u>y</u>er
gl<u>oo</u>m	**h<u>oo</u>k**	**n<u>au</u>ghty**

Complete the riddles with a rhyming word. The riddle's answer should have the same spelling pattern as the underlined vowel sound.

1. I rhyme with s<u>ou</u>ght, and I mean "____________________."
   I am "__________."
2. I rhyme with m<u>ou</u>nd, and I mean "____________________."
   I am "__________."
3. I rhyme with empl<u>oy</u>, and I mean "____________________."
   I am "__________."
4. I rhyme with gl<u>oo</u>m, and I mean "____________________."
   I am "__________."
5. I rhyme with h<u>oo</u>k, and I mean "____________________."
   I am "__________."

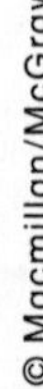

At Home: Together, make up additional riddles and challenge each other to guess the answers.

Name ______________________________

Read the following announcement made by the town crier in the land ruled by the greedy king in *Rumpelstiltskin's Daughter*. Fill in each blank with a vocabulary word. Use each word at least once.

coincidences	hobbled	mufflers	phase
prospered	sheepishly	sumptuous	sweeten

Hear ye! Hear ye! All those in the kingdom of the formerly greedy King are invited to a ________________ feast at the palace. The King has ________________ seen the errors of his ways. He realizes that he ________________ while his subjects starved and ________________ around with no shoes on their feet. He sends his sincerest apologies. (One hopes that "nice" is not just a ________________ that the King is going through!)

By the luckiest of ________________, the King at this time also invites all to join him in joyous celebration upon the election of one Hope Rumpelstiltskin to the position of Prime Minister of the kingdom. So put on your best ________________ and your dancing shoes and come to the palace at 8:00 tomorrow night. And to ________________ the pot, the King will give a gold coin to the first 100 peasants who walk through the new palace door. Please R.S.V.P. to the King by noon tomorrow.

Name ______________________________

Plan a sequel to *Rumpelstiltskin's Daughter.* The problem is given. Then tell how the problem will be solved. Write the events that will happen in the beginning, middle, and end of the story.

Problem: One of the King's former guards has discovered Hope's secret—her father, Rumpelstiltskin, is the one who knows how to spin straw into gold.

Title: ______________________________

Main characters: ______________________________

____

Setting: ______________________________

Beginning: ______________________________

____

____

Middle: ______________________________

____

____

____

____

____

End: ______________________________

____

____

____

At Home: Together, discuss the problems and solutions presented in other fairy tales with which everyone is familiar.

Name ______________________________

As you read *Rumpelstiltskin's Daughter*, fill in the Problem and Solution Chart.

Problem

Attempt	→	Outcome

Attempt	→	Outcome

Solution

How does the information you wrote in this Problem and Solution Chart help you monitor comprehension of *Rumpelstiltskin's Daughter*?

At Home: Have the student use the chart to retell the story.

Name ______________________________

As I read, I will pay attention to tempo.

"My father was a merchant before me, but he died when I
12 was a young man. Until then I had lived a life of comfort,
25 free of cares. Since I had my father's wealth in my hands, I
38 saw no need to change. But as I spent the money on foolish
51 pleasures, I did nothing to replace it. It was not too long
63 before I found that I had almost nothing left. I decided that the
76 only thing for me to do was to sell whatever remained of my
89 more valuable possessions and use the money to sail to other
100 lands. There I hoped to buy and sell merchandise, and not
111 come home until I had prospered enough to return to my
122 former life."
124 "Before I left here I bought some goods that I thought
135 I might exchange or sell on my journey and brought
145 them to the ship I was to sail on. Sailing with me were
158 other merchants who were of the same mind. At first the
169 voyage went well, and we were welcomed as businessmen
178 all over the world, landing and trading in many strange and
189 wonderful ports." 191

Comprehension Check

1. What was the man's problem? How did he solve it? **Problem and Solution**

2. How can you tell that the young man is determined? **Make Inferences**

	Words Read	–	Number of Errors	=	Words Correct Score
First Read		–		=	
Second Read		–		=	

At Home: Help the student read the passage, paying attention to the goal at the top of the page.

Name ______________________________

Greek and Roman gods and goddesses are familiar to us because of their names and stories. Many such as Venus have lent their names to familiar objects like planets. The chart lists some well-known gods and goddesses and a brief description of who they are.

Description	Greek Name	Roman Name
Moon goddess	Selene	Luna
Goddess of the hunt	Artemis	Diana
Goddess of love	Aphrodite	Venus
God of war	Ares	Mars
God of the sky and weather, main god	Zeus	Jupiter
God of the sea	Poseidon	Neptune

Write a myth. You can retell a myth you know or use the list of Roman and Greek gods and goddesses as you make up your own myth. Include at least one example of hyperbole and a moral in your story. Use another piece of paper if needed.

____

____

____

____

____

____

____

____

____

____

____

____

____

At Home: Together, discuss other myths or contexts in which you have heard the names of the Greek and Roman gods and goddesses.

Name ______________________________

Write the meaning of each idiom. Then use the idiom in a sentence. Use a dictionary or an on-line dictionary of idioms to help you find meanings.

1. all ears: definition: ______________________________
   sentence: ______________________________
   ____

2. can of worms: definition: ______________________________
   sentence: ______________________________
   ____

3. decked out: definition: ______________________________
   sentence: ______________________________
   ____

4. wake up on the wrong side of the bed: definition: ______________________________
   sentence: ______________________________
   ____

5. last straw: definition: ______________________________
   ____
   sentence: ______________________________
   ____

6. make a living: definition: ______________________________
   sentence: ______________________________
   ____

At Home: Together, discuss other familiar idioms such as *cry one's eyes out* or *play by ear.*

Name ______________________________

Sort the words in the box according to their syllable patterns. Divide each word into syllables by drawing lines.

advice	curtain	hundred	kindness	standpoint
childhood	follow	ignore	kingdom	supply
children	handsome	include	partner	surprise
complete	happen	increase	pattern	transform
counter	happy	instead	practice	window

VC/CV	VCC/CV	VC/CCV
1.	11.	18.
2.	12.	19.
3.	13.	20.
4.	14.	21.
5.	15.	22.
6.	16.	23.
7.	17.	24.
8.		25.
9.		
10.		

At Home: Together, discuss how paying attention to syllable patterns can help you read and spell longer words.

Name ______________________________

Create your own crossword puzzle using the vocabulary words. Once you have arranged the words in the puzzle and given them numbers, write clues for the words.

epidemic	intercept	outskirts	pedestrians
plight	quarantine	rendezvous	unbearable

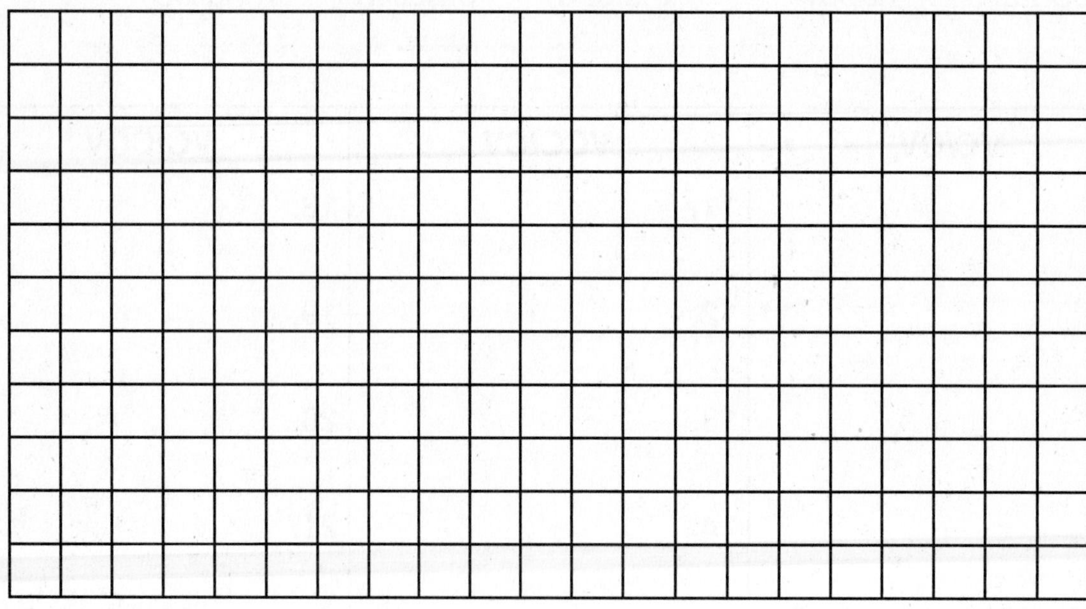

Across

____

____

____

____

Down

____

____

____

____

Name ____________________

The sentences in this review of *The Great Serum Race* are out of order. Think about rewriting the review so its sequence makes sense.

The story begins in 1925 in a small community outside Nome, Alaska, when Dr. Welch loses one patient after another to the highly infectious disease, diphtheria. To prevent the further spread of the disease, a quarantine went into effect. *The Great Serum Race* is a gripping tale of the race to bring diphtheria serum across the Alaskan wilderness from Anchorage to Nome. From Anchorage, the delicate bottles of serum first traveled 300 miles by steam engine. Winter in Alaska meant little light, much cold, and many storms. So a relay system of mushers and dog teams was established. The only way to cover the distance was by dog sled. Then they began their historic journey by sled to Nome. To save Nome they had to get diphtheria serum from Anchorage a thousand miles away. The city was spared a diphtheria epidemic.

Decide which sentences should be in the correct sequence. Write the first three words of each sentence to show the correct sequence of events.

1. ____________________
2. ____________________
3. ____________________
4. ____________________
5. ____________________
6. ____________________
7. ____________________
8. ____________________
9. ____________________
10. ____________________

At Home: Together, discuss other stories with heroic themes that you know about.

Practice

Comprehension: Sequence

Name ____________________

As you read *The Great Serum Race,* fill in the Sequence Chart.

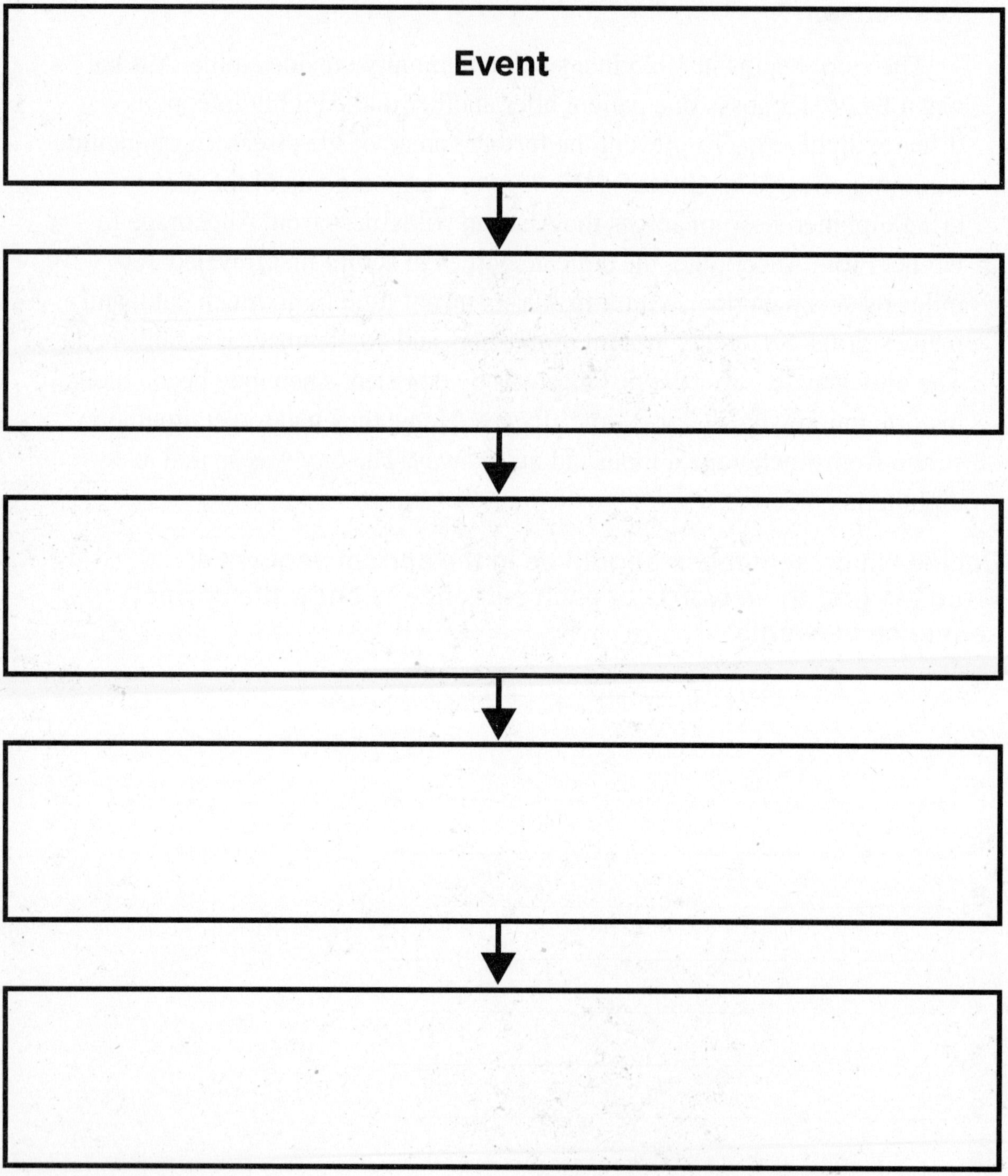

Event
↓
↓
↓
↓

How does the information you wrote in this Sequence Chart help you monitor comprehension of *The Great Serum Race*?

At Home: Have the student use the chart to retell the story.

As I read, I will pay attention to the pronunciation of vocabulary words and context clues.

On December 7, 1941, Japanese planes attacked American ships at
8 Pearl Harbor in Hawaii. The United States immediately joined the
18 Allies in Europe to fight in World War II. At the time, this country still
32 did not have any canines in the armed forces except for a few sled dogs.
47 A group of civilian, or non-military, dog experts thought that a war
59 dog training program should be started right away. Although some
69 military leaders were not interested at first, the group started a program
81 called Dogs for Defense in January 1942.
87 Dogs for Defense planned to recruit and train dogs to give to the
100 military. Many of these dogs would come from everyday Americans who
111 donated their pets to help the war effort. Thousands showed their
122 patriotism by bringing in their dogs. Even famous singers and actors of
134 the time donated beloved animals to help the cause. These pet owners
146 knew they might never see their dogs again.
154 When a dog was donated, the first step was an examination by
166 veterinarians. To avoid an epidemic of the disease rabies, all dogs were
178 given rabies shots. Each new dog was put into **quarantine** apart from
190 other dogs for 21 days. This was to make sure the animal didn't pass
203 on any illnesses the veterinarians might have missed. 211

Comprehension Check

1. How did Dogs for Defense start? **Sequence**

2. What problem did the military have? How did people try to solve it? **Problem and Solution**

	Words Read	–	Number of Errors	=	Words Correct Score
First Read		–		=	
Second Read		–		=	

At Home: Help the student read the passage, paying attention to the goal at the top of the page.

Name ________________________________

You are going to write a haiku about the Alaskan wilderness. First, brainstorm words of various numbers of syllables that are appropriate for your poem. Try to think of words that convey sensory information, are symbolic in some way, or that can be used in metaphors.

1 Syllable	2 Syllables	3 Syllables	4 Syllables
____	____	____	____
____	____	____	
____	____	____	
____	____		
____	____		
____	____		
____	____		

Now use this pattern to write your haiku about the Alaskan wilderness.

Line 1: 5 syllables

Line 2: 7 syllables

Line 3: 5 syllables

____

____

____

At Home: Together, write a haiku about something in nature or another topic.

Name ______________________________

Write a paragraph about the personal qualities it requires for a person to take action the way the mushers in *The Great Serum* race did. In your writing, use at least five pairs of synonyms.

____

____

____

____

____

____

____

____

____

____

____

____

____

Write the synonym pairs you used in your writing above.

1. ____________ ____________
2. ____________ ____________
3. ____________ ____________
4. ____________ ____________
5. ____________ ____________

At Home: Have a family "lightning round" in which one person says a word and another names a synonym as fast as he or she can.

Name ______________________

Practice

Phonics: V/CV, VC/V, and V/CV in Unstressed First Syllables

Think about *The Great Serum Race* to help you write at least 8 words that follow each syllable pattern. Use a dictionary, if needed, to check the syllable breaks. Write the words in the chart.

V/CV	VC/V	V/CV unstressed first syllable
1. ______	9. ______	17. ______
2. ______	10. ______	18. ______
3. ______	11. ______	19. ______
4. ______	12. ______	20. ______
5. ______	13. ______	21. ______
6. ______	14. ______	22. ______
7. ______	15. ______	23. ______
8. ______	16. ______	24. ______

For each syllable pattern, write one new word in a sentence. Underline the word you used as an example of the pattern. Then write a sentence that uses two of the words above.

25. V/CV: ______________________

____

26. VC/V: ______________________

____

27. V/CV unstressed first syllable: ______________________

____

28. ______________________

____

At Home: From the list above, explain why each word falls under a given syllable pattern.

Name ____________________

Complete each analogy. Use a dictionary or thesaurus if needed.

1. rendezvous : meeting :: resemblance : ____________
2. evacuate : return :: mitigate : ____________
3. inscribed : engraved :: enthralled : ____________
4. sumptuous : miserly :: spicy : ____________
5. vigil : watch :: regulation : ____________
6. pedestrians : walkers :: calamities : ____________
7. ravaged : protected :: prospered : ____________
8. unsatisfactory : excellent :: undone : ____________
9. mufflers : scarves :: pennants : ____________
10. grouchy : happy :: unbearable : ____________

Use both given vocabulary words in the same sentence.

1. embarrassment, coincidences ____________

2. plight, administer ____________

3. postmarked, sheepishly ____________

4. hobbled, intercept ____________

Name ______________________________

You are a radio announcer in 1925 sent to Nome to interview the musher who brings the diphtheria serum into the city. Write your interview. Use each vocabulary word in your interview.

broadcast	calculations	devastating	epidemic
marveled	outskirts	phase	quarantine

Name ______________________________

A. Use the etymology or history of the word to identify the vocabulary word.

employee	flourish	foreman	fulfill
gleefully	gritted	gloated	vigorously

1. This word comes from the Old English word *fullfyllan,* which means "to fill." ________________

2. This word is from the Old English word *grēot,* which means "sand."

____

3. This word comes from the Latin word *implicare,* which means "to enfold or involve."

____

4. This word comes from the Latin word *florēre,* which means "flower." ________________

5. This word comes from the Old English word *glēo,* which means "entertainment."

____

6. This word comes from the Old French word *vigor,* which means "strength." ________________

7. This word probably came from a Scandinavian language. It is similar to the Old Norse word *glotta,* which means "to grin scornfully." ________________

8. This word comes from the Old English words *fore* + *man,* which mean "in front" and "human being."

____

B. Choose two of the vocabulary words from above. Use each of them in a sentence.

9. ____

____

10. ____

____

____

Name ____________________

Practice

Comprehension: Character, Setting, Plot

It is 25 years after the events in *Juan Verdades.* Juan and Araceli Valdez are about to celebrate their 25th wedding anniversary. Use the story map below to plan a sequel to *Juan Verdades* and then write your story. Use another sheet of paper if needed.

Title: ____________________

Main characters and their traits: ____________________

____

____

____

Setting(s): ____________________

____

Problem: ____________________

____

Solution: ____________________

____

____

____

____

____

____

____

At Home: Discuss the story that your student wrote.

Name ______________________________

As you read *Juan Verdades,* fill in the Summary Chart.

Beginning	Middle	End

Summary

How does the information you wrote in this Summary Chart help you monitor comprehension of *Juan Verdades*?

At Home: Have the student use the chart to retell the story.

Name ______________________________

As I read I will pay attention to pauses, stops, and intonation.

When the first warm breeze hints of spring—*Yo-meni* to the Maidu
12 people—I like to sit near the lake on the Reservation. To be honest, it's
27 not much of a lake. I can easily swim across it from end to end. And when
44 the waves lap onto the pebbled shore, they carry things: soda cans, bottle
57 tops, an old sneaker, a chewed-up baseball bat, all splashing and bobbing
69 like they belong. Still, I sit and imagine I'm at Grassy Lake.
81 Two centuries ago, my ancestors camped all summer long at Grassy
92 Lake, where nothing splashed and bobbed but the salmon. Back then, life
104 and sustenance flourished in the foothills, streams, and mountains. Clear,
114 clean water cascaded down the falls, and fish swam along fresh streams
126 that carved out narrow canyons.
131 When Yo-meni settles over the Reservation, I try to see in the murky
144 water and hardscrabble grounds the same spirits—*kakini*—the old Maidu
155 saw at Grassy Lake. If I listen long enough, I can hear them whispering
169 through the tall weeds that overrun the field behind the school. Mostly
181 though, I just hear a used-up wind, proclaiming its loneliness.
191 One day, that old wind blew a girl named Cara Persad onto the
204 Reservation. Trust me, this was no cause for celebration. Especially for me.
216 She was going to live at our house "temporarily," and move into my room. 230

Comprehension Check

1. How can you tell that the narrator is a thoughtful and reflective thinker? **Character, Setting, Plot**

2. What does the narrator admire about the past? **Make Inferences**

	Words Read	–	Number of Errors	=	Words Correct Score
First Read		–		=	
Second Read		–		=	

At Home: Help the student read the passage paying attention to the goal at the top of the page.

Name ______________________________

These two maps show Mexico in 1824 and a current map of the American Southwest and Mexico. Compare both maps and write a paragraph about how Mexico and the American Southwest have changed since 1824.

____

____

____

____

____

____

____

____

____

____

____

____

____

____

____

At Home: Discuss with the student how the United States expanded westward.

Name ______________________________

For each base word given below, write as many words that have prefixes, suffixes, and/or inflectional endings as you can. Give yourself one point for each word that you write. Try to earn as many points as you can.

Base Word	Base Word + Prefixes/Suffixes/ Inflectional Endings	Points
1. plant	______________________________	____
	______________________________	
	______________________________	
	______________________________	
2. sweet	______________________________	____
	______________________________	
	______________________________	
	______________________________	
3. kind	______________________________	____
	______________________________	
	______________________________	
4. health	______________________________	____
	______________________________	
	______________________________	
	______________________________	
5. expect	______________________________	____
	______________________________	
	______________________________	
	______________________________	

At Home: Review the list of words that the student wrote. Together, brainstorm any other words that might be added to the list.

Name ____________________

All words of two or more syllables have accented syllables. Words of three or more syllables sometimes have more than one accented syllable. In a dictionary, a boldface accent mark ' indicates the syllable with greatest stress. The lesser-stressed syllable(s) are shown with lightface accent marks '. An example is the word *labyrinth*: lab'-y-rinth'

Read each word below to yourself. Listen to where you break the syllables and decide where the accent mark(s) should be placed. Write your syllabication and include accent marks. Then use a dictionary to confirm or correct the syllabication and placement of each accent mark.

Word	My Syllabication with Accents	Correct Syllabication with Accents
1. afternoon	____________	____________
2. magnificent	____________	____________
3. good-naturedly	____________	____________
4. confidently	____________	____________
5. convenient	____________	____________
6. conversation	____________	____________
7. wagonload	____________	____________
8. congratulate	____________	____________

At Home: Challenge your student to i´dentify the syllable breaks and placements of accents in the names of various friends.

Name ____________________

A. Write a synonym and an antonym for each vocabulary word.

1. limousine

synonym: ____________

antonym: ____________

2. embarked

synonym: ____________

antonym: ____________

3. promenade

synonym: ____________

antonym: ____________

4. unimaginable

synonym: ____________

antonym: ____________

5. sensational

synonym: ____________

antonym: ____________

6. extravagant

synonym: ____________

antonym: ____________

7. lamented

synonym: ____________

antonym: ____________

8. precarious

synonym: ____________

antonym: ____________

Choose two of the vocabulary words from above. Use each of them in a sentence.

9. ____________________

10. ____________________

Name ______________________________

Think about *Nothing Ever Happens on 90th Street.* Decide which of the following conclusions is valid or not valid and write a ✓ next to Yes or No. Support your answer with evidence from the text and from your knowledge and experience.

Conclusion	Valid?	Supporting Evidence
1. Nothing ever happens on 90th Street.	Yes No	
2. Eva's neighbors give her good advice about her writing.	Yes No	
3. Alexis is lonely at first.	Yes No	
4. Eva is friendly.	Yes No	

At Home: Discuss a story from a book, movie, or TV program and draw some conclusions from it.

Name ______________________________

As you read *Nothing Ever Happens on 90th Street,* fill in the Conclusions Chart.

What I Know	Text Evidence	Conclusions

How does the information you wrote in this Conclusions Chart help you monitor comprehension of *Nothing Ever Happens on 90th Street*?

At Home: Have the student use the chart to retell the story.

As I read, I will pay attention to punctuation.

Miss Carter gave us an assignment that I cannot possibly complete.
11 It's a writing assignment, and you know better than anyone how much I
24 love to write! After all, I share all my thoughts and secrets with you. If I
40 have an idea for a poem or a story, you're the first to know.
54 Why, even when I only have a little piece of an idea—Dad calls that
69 "a seed of inspiration"—I tell you first thing. I love that feeling of having
84 a good idea pop into my head, just like when I spot the first of the purple
101 lupines peeking through the fields of wild oats. When a good idea comes,
114 I run straight to you, don't I? Then I scribble it down while it is still as
131 fresh in my mind as the hot bread rolls Dad takes out of the oven on
147 Saturday night. Soup Night, he calls it, as if it were a big event. Well, it is
164 nice, but that's as much as I'll admit.
172 So why, dear Diary, have I lamented my sad fate, instead of cheering
185 another opportunity to do what I love doing anyway? Because this year
197 the theme of the school essay contest is "New and Exciting." Can you
210 believe it? I don't have a chance! 217

Comprehension Check

1. What mental images does the narrator make you see in her writing? **Make Inferences**

2. What is the narrator's problem? **Draw Conclusions**

	Words Read	–	Number of Errors	=	Words Correct Score
First Read		–		=	
Second Read		–		=	

At Home: Help the student read the passage paying attention to the goal at the top of the page.

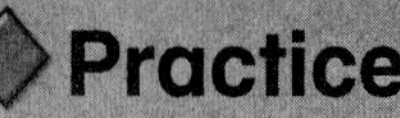

Name ______________________________

Eva's book about what happened on 90th Street that day has just been published. Now she is on a book tour and is coming to your town. You will be interviewing her for your school paper. Write a list of questions and follow-up questions that you would ask her during your interview.

1. ______________________________
2. ______________________________
3. ______________________________
   ____
4. ______________________________
5. ______________________________
   ____
6. ______________________________
7. ______________________________
   ____
8. ______________________________
   ____
9. ______________________________
10. ______________________________
   ____

At Home: Have the student practice interviewing skills by interviewing you or another family member.

Name ______________________________

Be a word history detective. In a dictionary, look at the word histories of each word. Show how the words in the group are related or not related.

1. act, active, agitate, agent, agile

____

____

2. sensation, sense, sentence, sentiment

____

____

____

3. advice, advise, aviation, aviary

____

____

____

____

____

____

4. customer, custom, costume

____

____

____

At Home: Have the student use a dictionary to look up the origins of words you select.

Name ______________________________

A. Write a word with a final /ər/ that fits each clue.

1. A person who works on stage. ______________
2. A person who performs ballet. ______________
3. A baby rides in this. ______________
4. What people feel when they see an accident. ______________
5. Green vegetables used in salad. ______________

B. Now make up clues for words with a final /ər/ of your choice. The word you choose should have the spelling of the final /ər/ sound that is shown in parentheses.

6. (ar) Clue: ______________________________
____
7. (er) Clue: ______________________________
______________________ ______________
8. (er) Clue: ______________________________
____
9. (or) Clue: ______________________________
______________________ ______________
10. (ur) Clue: ______________________________
______________________ ______________

At Home: Brainstorm other words with a final /ər/. Then have the student create clues for those words.

Name ______________________________

A. Write a definition and sample sentence for each vocabulary word.

1. nonrenewable ______________________________

2. renewable ______________________________

3. adverse ______________________________

4. generate ______________________________

5. apparatus ______________________________

B. Choose three of the vocabulary words from above. Use them all in one sentence. Underline each vocabulary word in your sentence.

6. ______________________________

At Home: T/K

Name ____________________

There are different kinds of **cause-and-effect** relationships. Sometimes a cause will have multiple effects. Sometimes an effect has many causes. Sometimes a cause creates a series of effects.

Use these charts to show causes and effects that you read about in *Building Green* as well as any prior knowledge you have about the subjects.

1. Describe the effects of digging up fossil fuels to burn for our energy needs.

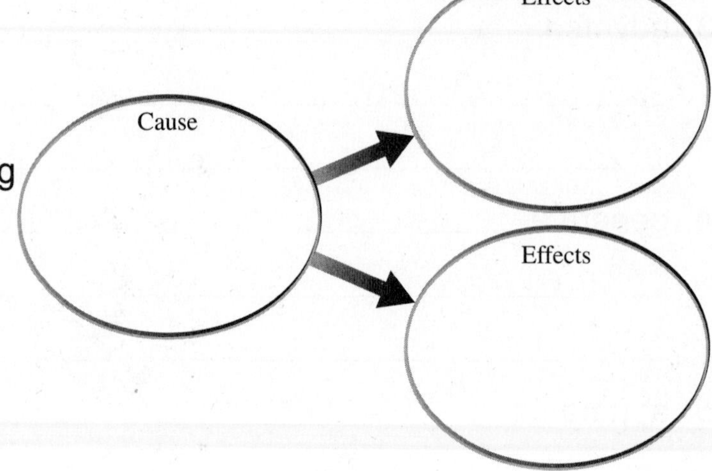

2. Describe how we get the wind for wind energy.

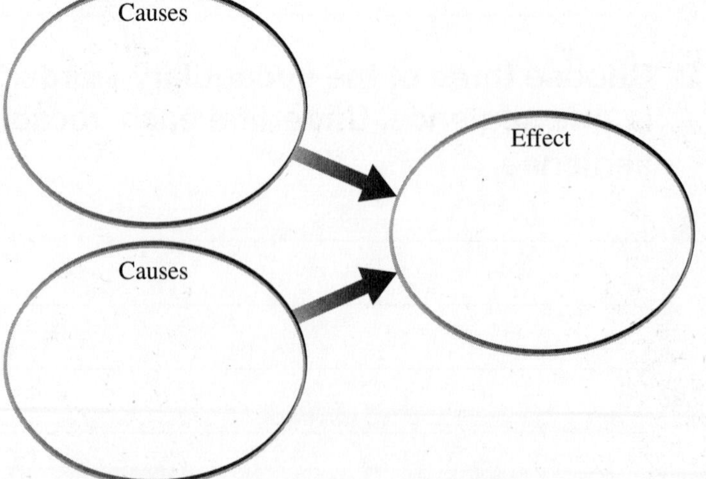

At Home: Discuss with your student alternative sources of energy.

Name ____________________

As you read *Building Green,* fill in the Cause and Effect Chart.

Cause	→	Effect
	→	
	→	
	→	

How does the information you wrote in this Cause and Effect Chart help you monitor comprehension of *Building Green*?

At Home: Have the student use the chart to retell the story.

Name ____

As I read, I will pay attention to the pronunciation of vocabulary and other difficult words.

Did you ever put something off until the last minute? Maybe it was a
14 school project. You were given all week to do it. That seemed like a lot of
30 time, but the week sped by. Before you knew it, you were down to one
45 day and hadn't even started. You worked fast and furiously. You finished
57 on time, but you know you could have done a better job. You regretted not
72 starting earlier.
74 Some people think the United States and other nations around the
85 world are putting off a project, too. And if we don't start working harder
99 on it soon, we will regret it. The project is a big one—developing clean,
114 **renewable** energy sources.
117 Today, the world depends mostly on coal, oil, and natural gas to power
130 our lives. These fossil fuels produce electricity, gasoline, and heating oil.
141 They also cause big problems. Burning coal and oil pours gases into the
154 air. These gases have many adverse effects on the environment. They
165 cause smog, acid rain, and other kinds of pollution. The gases also may
178 be changing worldwide climate patterns. Furthermore, these fuels are
187 **nonrenewable**. We have only so much of them. They will run out
199 some day. 201

Comprehension Check

1. On what does the world depend for power? What is the effect of this dependence? **Cause and Effect**

2. How do you know whom the author is trying to persuade? **Persuasion**

	Words Read	–	Number of Errors	=	Words Correct Score
First Read		–		=	
Second Read		–		=	

At Home: Help the student read the passage paying attention to the goal at the top of the page.

Name ________________________________

Study Strategies make your work easier.
Skimming material means you look over material to get a general idea of what it is about. Do not read every word. Look at headings, boldfaced words, italicized terms, pictures, and other items that stand out.
Scanning material means you think of some key words and read quickly to find those words. This often leads you to some useful information.
Taking notes helps you remember important facts and details. Write down important dates and terms. If you make your notes on index cards, you can organize them easily.
Outlining the main idea and the supporting details helps you master information. Use a formal outline or an informal one.

Choose a chapter or section from your social studies or science book. or use a newspaper or magazine article. Then make an outline in the space below.

____

____

____

____

____

____

____

____

____

____

____

____

____

At Home: Discuss how the student might study more efficiently.

Practice

Vocabulary Strategy: Context Clues Within a Sentence

Name ______________________________

Rewrite each sentence to provide a context clue within the sentence for the underlined word(s). Use definitions, restatements, or synonyms as your clues.

1. Many people build homes that are <u>ecologically friendly</u>.

____

____

2. To reduce heat loss, builders use <u>insulation</u>.

____

____

3. <u>Solar</u> energy provides the power for many homes.

____

____

4. Today's builders are building more <u>energy-efficient</u> homes than ever before.

____

____

____

5. Dark-color tiles placed near windows <u>absorb</u> heat energy.

____

____

6. Straw became a local building material on the <u>tree-barren</u> prairie.

____

____

____

At Home: Encourage the student to study vocabulary words in other subject areas by using each word in a sentence that includes a context clue.

Name ______________________________

Write final /ən/ or final /əl/ words to complete the crossword puzzle.

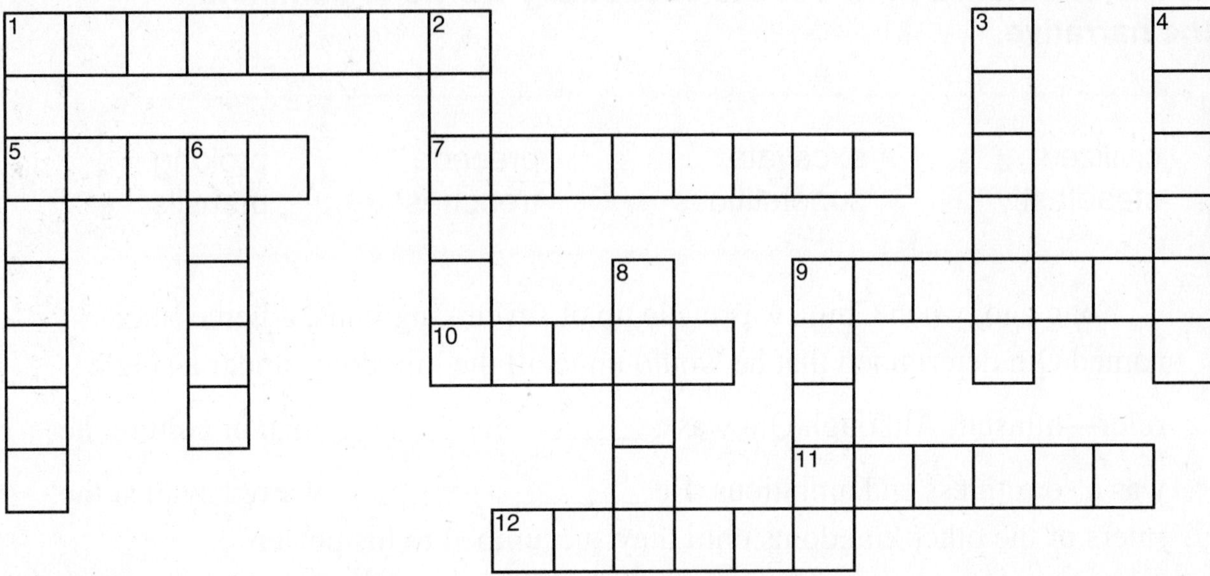

Across

1. past perfect form of *forgive*
5. an antonym for *urban*
7. plural of *child*
9. having to do with medicine
10. a sour, yellow fruit
11. real
12. a writing tool that uses graphite

Down

1. strong
2. a coin worth five cents
3. a small desert rodent
4. twice as much
6. terrible
8. a small bird with a red chest
9. a picture that is painted on a wall

At Home: Have the student analyze the final /əl/ and final /ən/ words in the crossword for any helpful spelling patterns.

Name ______________________________

This nonfiction narrative about Qin Shihuang, emperor of China has blanks in it. Use the vocabulary words to complete the narrative.

civilized	excavate	precede	prolong
steadfastly	superstitious	trenches	utensils

Long ago, when China was made up of seven kingdoms, a fierce ruler named Qin determined that he would unite all the kingdoms under a single ruler—himself. Although Qin was a __________________ man of culture, he was also ruthless and ambitious. He __________________ warred against the rulers of the other kingdoms until they succumbed to his power.

Qin was also a __________________ man. He believed that when he died, his life would go on. Work had begun on an elaborate underground tomb whose initial construction would __________________ Qin's death by many decades. __________________ were dug and expanded as workers began to __________________ Qin's final resting place.

As the years passed, Qin's tomb became a palace, outfitted with all that he would need after death—from a magnificent bronze map of the world to the most mundane __________________ for everyday living. Though he did everything that the science of his day told him would __________________ his life, Qin Shihuang, was after all mortal. His tomb, though incomplete, was standing waiting for him to enter one final time after he died.

Name ____________________

Write a summary based on the informal outline below.

- In 1974 three men were digging a well in China and found a clay man's head.
- Archaeologists discovered thousands of buried clay soldiers, complete with weapons.
- The first emperor of China was Qin Shihuang (259–210 B.C.), who had successfully united seven separate kingdoms.
- He declared himself ruler over approximately one million square miles and chose the name "First Emperor, God in Heaven, and Almighty of the Universe."
- Qin died while on a tour of his lands and was buried in an extravagant tomb that had been under construction since Qin's youth.
- The current government of China refuses to let archaeologists disturb Qin's tomb.
- Experts speculate that although Qin's body would not have been mummified, it was likely encased in a suit made of jade because people believed that jade kept bodies from decomposing.

At Home: Review with the student the summary he or she wrote.

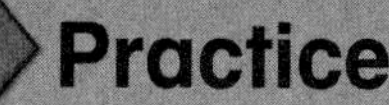

Name ______________________________

Comprehension: Summarize

As you read *The Emperor's Silent Army*, fill in the Summary Chart.

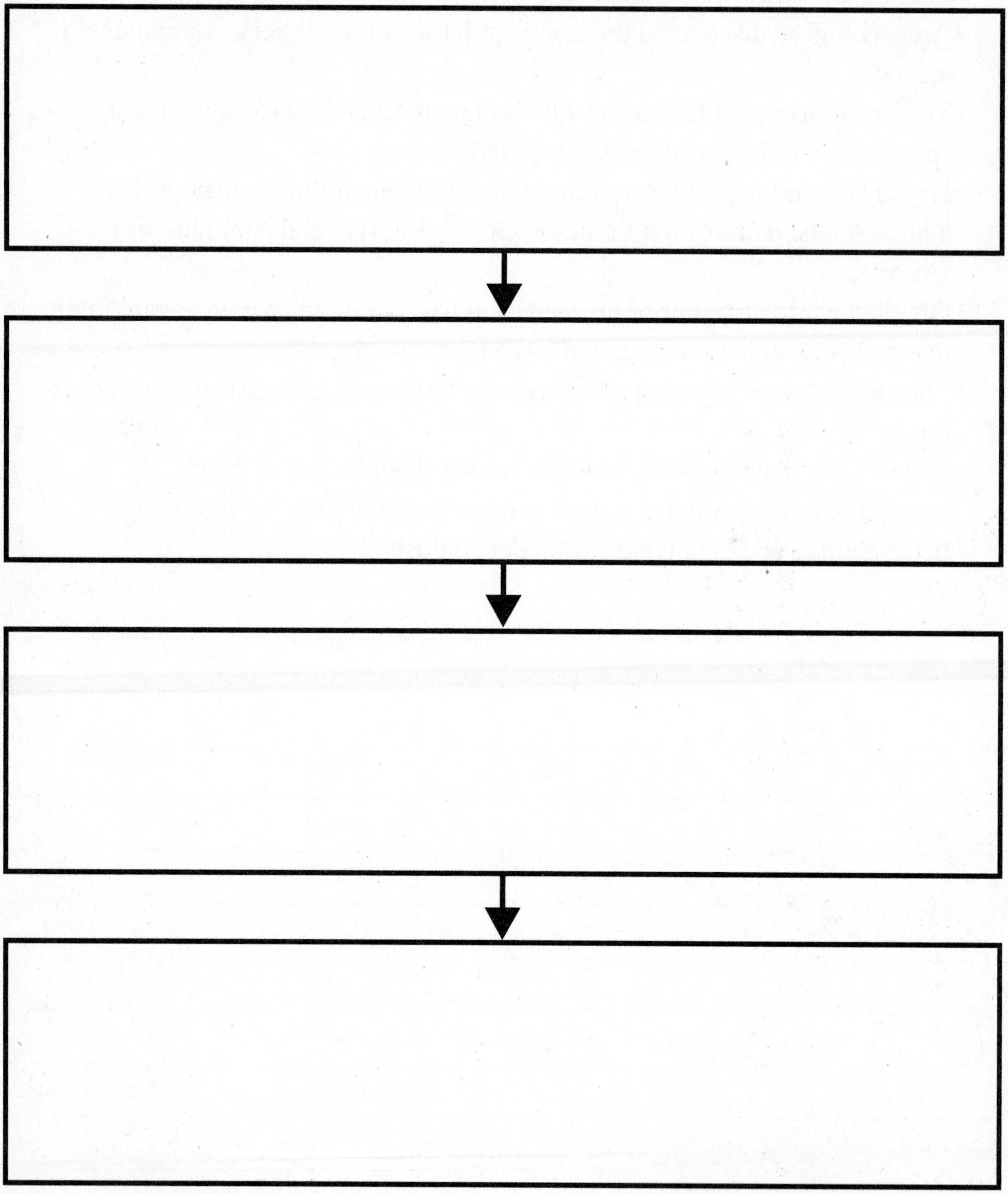

How does the information you wrote in this Summary Chart help you monitor comprehension of *The Emperor's Silent Army*?

At Home: Have the student use the chart to retell the story.

Name ______________________________

As I read, I will pay attention to tempo or expression.

Way out in the middle of the Pacific Ocean, there is a small island.
14 It is not near anything. South America and Australia are each at least
27 1,000 miles away. The island's Polynesian name is Rapa Nui
36 (RA-pa NOO-ee).
36 Rapa Nui was created by three erupting volcanoes that burst out of the
49 sea to form a triangular island with steep hills and huge craters. The first
63 Polynesian settlers came to the island more than 1,700 years ago.
73 A Polynesian culture flourished there for over 1,000 years, but
82 eventually it dwindled away. Only a small population of people still lived
94 there. The island was unknown to most people until Easter Day 1722.
105 On that day three Dutch ships led by Captain Jacob Roggeveen
116 rediscovered and renamed the island. Easter Island was suddenly back on
127 the map. This history of the island was still a mystery to the explorers,
141 but one thing was very clear. The island was home to hundreds of the most
156 enormous statues any of them had ever seen.
164 The statues dotted the coastline of the island. Who had carved them? How
177 did they do it? Anthropologists and archaeologists have pieced together
187 evidence that Polynesians from somewhere else in the South Pacific
197 relocated to Rapa Nui. Dozens of settlers must have loaded up their large
210 double canoes with food, water, animals, tools, and plants to help them
222 survive in their new home. 227

Comprehension Check

1. Summarize the history of Rapa Nui. **Summarize**

2. Who do you think made the giant statues? **Draw Conclusions**

	Words Read	–	Number of Errors	=	Words Correct Score
First Read		–		=	
Second Read		–		=	

At Home: Help the student read the passage, paying attention to the goal at the top of the page.

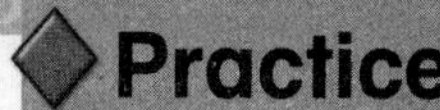

Name ______________________________

Lyric poetry expresses a feeling or captures a moment in time. It uses **meter,** the arrangement of alternating stressed and unstressed syllables, as in: (stressed syllables are in capitals)
I WENT to TOWN and PARKED my BIKE aGAINST the CURB.
Iambic pentameter, or five pairs of stressed/unstressed syllables, is the most common meter, as in the phrase above.
Lyric poetry also uses **consonance**, the repetition of a consonant sound at the beginning or end of syllables, as in: I will click the lock to check the clock.

Choose a topic for a lyric poem. You might write about Qin or about another person who had a great idea. Write a lyric poem in iambic pentameter about your topic. Use the pattern lines below to help you write ten syllables per line with the accent on the second syllable in each pair.

______/______/______/

______/______

______/______/______/

______/______

______/______/______/

______/______

______/______/______/

______/______

______/______/______/

______/______

______/______/______/

______/______

At Home: Discuss with the student what he or she found most pleasurable or most difficult in writing lyric poetry.

Name ______________________________

A. Sort the words in each group according to the meanings of the prefixes. Use a dictionary if needed.

1. rewind replace reusable
return rework redo

re- meaning "back"	*re-* meaning "again"
______________	______________
______________	______________
______________	______________

2. untangle unlock unequal
unclear unsafe unscrambled

un- meaning "not"	*un-* meaning "opposite of"
______________	______________
______________	______________
______________	______________

B. Choose one word to show the meaning of each prefix above. Write each word in a sentence and underline the word you used.

3. ______________________________
____

4. ______________________________
____

5. ______________________________
____

6. ______________________________
____

At Home: Choose one of the prefixes above and brainstorm other words that have that prefix.

Name ______________________________

A. For each prefix, write an example and the meaning of your example.

un- Example: unhappy Meaning: not happy

Prefix	Example	Meaning
1. *un-*	______________	______________
2. *il-*	______________	______________
3. *dis-*	______________	______________
4. *re-*	______________	______________
5. *super-*	______________	______________
6. *extra-*	______________	______________
7. *pro-*	______________	______________
8. *anti-*	______________	______________
		______________
9. *bi-*	______________	______________
10. *en-*	______________	______________

B. Write a sentence for four of the example words you wrote above.

11. ____

____

12. ____

____

13. ____

____

14. ____

____

At Home: Together choose one of the prefixes above and think of as many words that have that prefix as possible.

Name ______________________________

Latisha Walker from *The Case of the Phantom Poet* decides to write a cover letter to give to the principal with her article for the competition. Write that letter using each of the vocabulary words at least once.

anonymous	array	charismatic	despondently
significance	sleuthing	sponsoring	mimics

Name ______________________________

Read the passage. Write two conclusions that you can draw from the story. Then list facts or examples from the passage or your own personal experience that support your conclusions.

Mr. Garcia was stumped. The principal had asked the two student finalists for a writing competition to write an article about an inspirational person. Both girls, Mackenzie and Amber, had written excellent essays. The writing in both was clear and lively. No errors could be found in either piece. Mackenzie had written about the town's mayor, who has been honored in many ways by both the school and the town over the years. He was a classic inspirational leader to choose.

Amber's essay, on the other hand, was a complete surprise. Not only had she chosen an unconventional person for her article, the team's mascot, but she also had to spend some of her valuable time just figuring out the mascot's identity. Mr. Garcia had a tough decision to make. Both were fine essays, but which one was the winner?

1. Conclusion: ______________________________

____

Support: ______________________________

____

____

____

2. Conclusion: ______________________________

____

Support: ______________________________

____

____

____

At Home: Together, discuss any other conclusions you can draw from the passage.

Name ______________________________

As you read *The Case of the Phantom Poet,* fill in the Conclusions Chart.

Text Clues	Conclusion

How does the information you wrote in this Conclusions Chart help you monitor comprehension of *The Case of the Phantom Poet*?

At Home: Have the student use the chart to retell the story.

Name ______________________________

As I read, I will pay attention to dialogue, tempo, and intonation.

SCENE 1: The first day of school

7 **NARRATOR:** The school year is beginning at the Benny Goodman
17 Middle School. Ms. Steinberg, the school's orchestra leader, sits at her
28 desk reviewing her class listing, and sighs.
35 **MS. STEINBERG:** I hope either Dylan Boone or Patti Hersh took up
47 another instrument this summer. They're both excellent clarinet players,
56 but they just don't cooperate with each other. Patti and Dylan are like oil
70 and water. Instead of playing the music together, they end up playing over
83 and against each other. And I see we're going to have another clarinet
96 player this year, too–Tim Ng. Well, it will be an interesting year.
109 **NARRATOR:** The door to the classroom flies open. Dylan and Patti try
121 to push through the doorway at the same time. They are arguing–as usual.
131 **DYLAN:** Do you mind, Patti–I was here first. Ms. Steinberg–Patti's pushing!
144 **PATTI:** No, you weren't, because you are never first at anything. Ms.
156 Steinberg–please tell Dylan to mind his manners and let me in!
168 **MS. STEINBERG:** I've got a better suggestion. Why don't both
178 of you move so the newest addition to our class can come in?
191 **NARRATOR:** Dylan and Patti turn around in surprise. Tim Ng stands
202 behind them. 204

Comprehension Check

1. What problem does Ms. Steinberg have? **Summarize**

2. What surprise does Ms. Steinberg have in store for Dylan and Patti? **Draw Conclusions**

	Words Read	–	Number of Errors	=	Words Correct Score
First Read		–		=	
Second Read		–		=	

At Home: Help the student read the passage paying attention to the goal at the top of the page.

Practice

Text Feature: Tables

Name ______________________________

Your class plans to perform a play. Write a description of each job. Here are few typical jobs needed to put on a play. Add other jobs you think might be needed as you think about plays.

Job Title	Job Description
1. Actors	
2. Director	
3. Prop manager	
4. Stage hands	
5. ____________	

At Home: Discuss plays you and the student have seen or performed in.

Name ______________________________

Write a synonym to complete each analogy. Use a thesaurus or dictionary as needed.

1. competition : contest :: winner : ________
2. dare : challenge :: follow : ________
3. charismatic : charming :: confident : ________
4. shock : stun :: creative : ________
5. consume : devour :: devastate : ________
6. sadly : unhappily :: annoying : ________
7. ignore : disregard :: throw : ________
8. welcome : greeting :: courtesy : ________
9. case : mystery :: difficulty : ________
10. scheme : trick :: treacherous : ________

Write your own analogy that uses synonyms.

11. ________ : ________ ::
________ : ________

12. ________ : ________ ::
________ : ________

At Home: Have the student explain the analogies he or she wrote on the second part of the page.

Name ____________________

Add *-ion* or *-ation* to each base word in the box to make a new word. Write a sentence that includes each word with a suffix.

act	confuse	connect	consider	discuss
form	inform	innovate	recommend	relax

1. ____________________

2. ____________________

3. ____________________

4. ____________________

5. ____________________

6. ____________________

7. ____________________

8. ____________________

9. ____________________

10. ____________________

At Home: Together, brainstorm words that end in *-ion* and *-ation*.

Name ______________________________

Write the clues for the vocabulary words in the puzzle.

1. a	n	o	n	y	m	o	u	2. s						3. g					
p								4. l	a	m	e	n	t	e	d				
5. p	r	o	m	e	n	a	d	e						n					
a								u				6. p	r	e	c	e	d	e	
r				7. a				t						r					
8. a	d	v	e	r	s	e		h	e		9. e	m	b	a	r	k	e	d	
t				r				i						t					
u				a				10. n	o	n	r	e	n	e	w	a	b	l	e
s				y				g											

Across

1. ______________________

4. ______________________

5. ______________________

6. ______________________

8. ______________________

9. ______________________

10. ______________________

Down

1. ______________________

____

2. ______________________

3. ______________________

7. ______________________

A. Label the vocabulary words in the box according to their parts of speech. Use *n.* for noun, *v.* for verb, *adj.* for adjective, and *adv.* for adverb.

charismatic	______	civilized	______	despondently	______
employee	______	excavate	______	extravagant	______
flourish	______	foreman	______	fulfill	______
gleefully	______	gloated	______	gritted	______
limousine	______	mimics	______	precarious	______
prolong	______	renewable	______	sensational	______
significance	______	sponsoring	______	steadfastly	______
superstitious	______	trenches	______	unimaginable	______
utensils	______	vigorously	______		

B. Write four sentences using the vocabulary words in the box. Try to include as many vocabulary words in your sentences as you can. Underline each vocabulary word that you use.

1. ______________________________

____

____

2. ______________________________

____

____

3. ______________________________

____

4. ______________________________

____

____

Name ______________________________

Some people have learned to climb mountains despite being vision impaired. Write questions you have about such an achievement. Use each vocabulary word once.

awesome	deterioriated	guidance	maturity
peripheral	specialists	summit	typical

1. ______________________________

____

2. ______________________________

____

3. ______________________________

____

4. ______________________________

____

5. ______________________________

____

6. ______________________________

____

7. ______________________________

____

8. ______________________________

____

Name ______________________________

Write a paragraph for each given purpose.

1. Write to inform. ______________________________

2. Write to persuade. ______________________________

At Home: Together, discuss authors' purposes for writing various materials such as textbooks or magazines.

Name ____________________

Practice

Comprehension: Author's Purpose

As you read "Seeing Things His Own Way," fill in the Author's Purpose Chart.

Clues	Author's Purpose

How does the information you wrote in this Author's Purpose Chart help you monitor comprehension of "Seeing Things His Own Way"?

At Home: Have the student use the chart to retell the story.

Name ____________________

As I read, I will pay attention to pauses, stops, and intonations.

The 1930s was a difficult decade for Americans. Under the cloud of
11 the Great Depression, the average American learned to do without
21 comforts and luxuries. Many even had to live without necessities. By
32 comparison our lives today are easy. Most of us can shop at well-stocked
45 grocery stores, fill our gas tanks whenever we need to, and watch
57 television to take our minds off of the pressures of everyday life.
69 In the 1930s people were lucky to have even a low paying job. Many
82 were unemployed, impoverished, and frightened. They didn't
89 know how they would feed their families or pay their rent. Many people
102 became homeless. Those fortunate enough to have radios listened
111 to them hoping to hear good news.
118 One piece of good news came in an unexpected package. In 1933 a
130 racehorse named Seabiscuit was born. His owners had high hopes that he
142 would become a champion. He was, after all, the son of a champion. But
156 Seabiscuit was not a **typical** racehorse. He was the ultimate underdog.
167 Homely, short, stubborn, awkward, and hard to train, he was the unlikeliest
179 hero. That's why everyone loved him.
185 Then in 1936, during a dark period in American history, people finally
196 had something to cheer about. Seabiscuit got serious. He got some long
108 overdue attention and care. He got motivated. He got in shape. And he
121 started to win. 224

Comprehension Check

1. Why were the 1930s so difficult? **Summarize**

2. What was Seabiscuit's contribution to the nation? **Make Inferences**

	Words Read	–	Number of Errors	=	Words Correct Score
First Read		–		=	
Second Read		–		=	

At Home: Help the student read the passage paying attention to the goal at the top of the page.

Name ____________________

The device below enlarges print so that it is large enough to read. Look at the diagram and accompanying labels. Then write a paragraph to introduce and describe the product.

Big type helps people who have trouble

Color or black-and-white monitor switch

On/off switch

Magnification paddle

Focus adjustment knob

Reading platform

Big type helps people who have trouble reading small fonts

Sliding lever

At Home: Together, discuss a diagram and its labels that is in an instruction booklet for a household appliance.

Name ______________________________

A vision-impaired climber is speaking at your school. You have been selected to introduce her to the students. Use a synonym from the box to help support each underlined context clue.

support	challenging	pursuing	navigate	barriers
rugged	erode	astonishing	treacherous	applaud

Most mountain climbers can chart a course during the day, but they might find it impossible to ______________ a mountain in the dark. While that might seem dangerous to most climbers, Nancy doesn't think it is ______________ at all. Her sight began to disintegrate when she was young, but her spirit did not ______________. Nancy's struggle to live a normal life and then go beyond has led her to find the stimulating and ______________ hobby of mountain climbing. She has climbed to the peak of the world's harshest and most ______________ mountain, Mount Everest.

When she was growing up, she learned to live with frustration, but it did not keep her from going after her goals and ______________ her dreams. With the assistance and ______________ of her friends and family, Nancy overcame obstacles and ______________ alike. Let's clap and ______________ Nancy's amazing efforts and listen to her ______________ feats. Please welcome Nancy Johnson to this auditorium.

At Home: Help the student create an introduction using synonyms as context clues.

Name ______________________

Practice

Phonics: More Words with *-ion* Spelling Changes

Write the given base word with the *-ion* suffix. Then use each group of four *-ion* words in a rhyme. Use a dictionary if needed.

1. extend ______________
2. suspend ______________
3. apprehend ______________
4. comprehend ______________

____

____

____

____

5. permit ______________
6. admit ______________
7. emit ______________
8. transmit ______________

____

____

____

____

9. perceive ______________
10. misconceive ______________
11. deceive ______________
12. receive ______________

____

____

____

____

At Home: Discuss the meanings of words that have spelling changes when the suffix *-ion* is added.

Name ________________________________

Look at the words in the crossword puzzle frame and then write clues to accompany the puzzle.

clockwise	edgy	formations	hovering
interior	seered	wreckage	intact

	1 h										
2 f	o	r	m	a	t	i	o	n	3 s		
	v								e		
	e								v		
4 w	r	e	c	k	a	g	e		e		
	i								r		
5 i	n	t	e	r	6 i	o	r		e		
	g				n			7 e	d	g	y
					t						
					a						
		8 c	l	o	c	k	w	i	s	e	
					t						

Across

2. ______________________________

4. ______________________________
____

5. ______________________________

7. ______________________________

8. ______________________________
____

Down

1. ______________________________
____

3. ______________________________

6. ______________________________

Robert Ballard did not want to take anything from the remains of the *Titanic*. Instead he left a memorial plaque on the ship to honor those people who died in the tragedy. Others have not been as sentimental about the wreck and have taken many souvenirs from the site. What is your opinion? Is it okay or not okay to take souvenirs from the wreckage of the *Titanic*? Write a paragraph to express your opinion. Include facts, reasons, and examples to support your opinion.

____

____

____

____

____

____

____

____

____

____

Number each sentence in the paragraph you wrote above. Write the number of each sentence on the line to show if it states a fact, an opinion, or both facts and opinions.

1. Facts: ______________

2. Opinions: ______________

3. Facts and Opinions: ______________

At Home: Together, discuss news stories from newspapers, TV, or the radio. Try to distingush fact from opinion.

Name ____________________

As you read *Exploring the Titanic*, fill in the Fact and Opinion Chart.

Fact	Opinion

How does the information you wrote in this Fact and Opinion Chart help you monitor comprehension of *Exploring the Titanic*?

At Home: Have the student use the chart to retell the story.

Name ______________________________

As I read, I will pay attention to punctuation.

Great pioneers of oceanography like Jacques Cousteau led the way. In
11 the 1960s he was at the height of his fame. A new generation of ocean
25 explorers was following his lead.
30 One of the brightest new stars was Robert Ballard. His adventurous
41 spirit and quick grasp of promising new technology helped him achieve
52 great things!
54 Ballard's first taste of adventure at sea occurred in his teens. When
66 he was in high school he had the chance to work for a summer at the
82 Scripps Institution of Oceanography in San Diego. With some other
92 young people, Ballard helped gather scientific data aboard a research
102 ship called the *Orca*.
106 On one trip the *Orca* was hit by one of the worst storms in years. The
122 ship rose up the steep sides of giant swells, and then it plunged down the
137 other side! The intensity of the storm scared and exhilarated Ballard. He
149 climbed to the ship's bridge to ride out the storm with the captain. The
163 bridge was the highest spot on board. Because of its height, it was tossed
177 even more wildly than the rest of the boat.
186 At the end of the summer **Ballard** was happy to step back on dry land.
201 Yet he felt a kind of pride, too. The sea had tested him, and he had
217 passed. 218

Comprehension Check

1. What opinion does the author have about Ballard? **Fact and Opinion**

2. Why was oceanography a good choice for Ballard? **Make Inferences**

	Words Read	–	Number of Errors	=	Words Correct Score
First Read		–		=	
Second Read		–		=	

At Home: Help the student read the passage, paying attention to the goal at the top of the page.

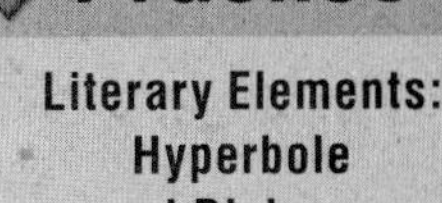

Name ______________________________

Pecos Bill is a larger-than-life character featured in many tall tales. Read this passage about Pecos Bill and then change the underlined words into hyperbole. Use another piece of paper if needed.

Pecos Bill was the greatest cowboy who ever lived. He could ride a stallion that was (1) really ornery, but Pecos Bill needed a challenge. He had heard about the wild tornadoes of Kansas, so he decided to tame one of those. He didn't want to ride just any puny twister. He waited until the meanest, darkest, most powerful tornado rode across Kansas. When it finally roared into town, (2) it was really loud. The funnel cloud was (3) tall and (4) wide. But Pecos Bill just jumped on top of that twister and rode it like it was (5) a tame horse.

Of course the twister didn't like having Pecos Bill on top. It roared across Kansas and into Texas. Along the way it swirled up rivers here and there (6) causing them to twist. The tornado bucked its way across the Southwest where it rained (7) a lot and carved the Grand Canyon. After a while the tornado had nothing left. Pecos Bill dropped to the ground and pushed the ground in (8) so deep that he made the lowest point in the country—Death Valley.

1. ______________________________
____
2. ______________________________
3. ______________________________
4. ______________________________
____
5. ______________________________
6. ______________________________
7. ______________________________
8. ______________________________

At Home: Discuss with the student other tall tales that either of you know about.

Name ______________________________

Write four more words that have the same suffix as each given word. Then use all five words in one or more related sentences. You may add additional prefixes, suffixes, and inflectional endings to your words as needed.

weightless

1. ____________________ **3.** ____________________

2. ____________________ **4.** ____________________

____

____

____

____

____

____

flowerlike

5. ____________________ **7.** ____________________

6. ____________________ **8.** ____________________

At Home: Have the student use more suffixes, such as *-age, -ize,* and *–ive.*

Name ______________________

Read the pronunciation of each word. Then write the word and use it in a sentence. Use a dictionary if needed.

1. blok´ij ______________

____

2. im pres´iv ______________

____

3. ak´tiv ______________

____

____

4. em´fə sīz ______________

____

5. pər sen´ tij ______________

____

____

6. di struk´ tiv ______________

____

____

7. rek´ij ______________

____

8. mə môr´ē ə līz ______________

____

____

At Home: Together, brainstorm other words that have the suffixes *-ive*, *-age*, and *-ize*.

Name ______________________

Answer the questions to show your understanding of the underlined vocabulary words.

bewildering	moderate	hamper	prohibit	accessible

1. What is something that is bewildering to you? Explain why.

____

____

2. What is something that you feel should be consumed only in a moderate amount?

____

____

3. What might hamper you from saving your money this year?

____

____

4. If you could prohibit one bad habit that you have, what would it be? Why?

____

____

5. What is something that is accessible to you without a car?

____

____

Name ____________________________

Read about two summer internships that help people who are visually impaired or hearing impaired. Circle the parts of each job description you would like to do. Then write a paragraph about the internship that you would choose and why.

Hearing-Impaired Nonprofit Center in Los Angeles, CA	Vision-Impaired Advocacy Foundation in Washington, D.C.
Use sign language to greet visitors.	Answer phones and open mail.
Answer phones and open mail for the center.	Make arrangements for visually or hearing-impaired visitors.
Assist hearing-impaired adults who are looking for employment.	Greet visitors and politicians and provide refreshments.
Check out technology equipment to center participants and provide help and answer questions if needed.	Help draft brochures on issues affecting the visually impaired.
Create program to share sign language with both the hearing-impaired community and the outside community.	Help organize benefit to honor recipients who have been recognized by the foundation.
Help with a summer day-care camp program for children who are hearing impaired.	Read daily newspapers to brief lobbyists on events that may affect the foundation.
Organize end-of-the-summer picnic for the community and center participants.	Assist foundation's librarian with reshelving books and archiving relevant news articles.

____

____

____

____

____

____

At Home: Together, discuss ways to compare and contrast two activities you both like to do.

Name ______________________________

As you read *Saving Grace,* fill in the Venn Diagram.

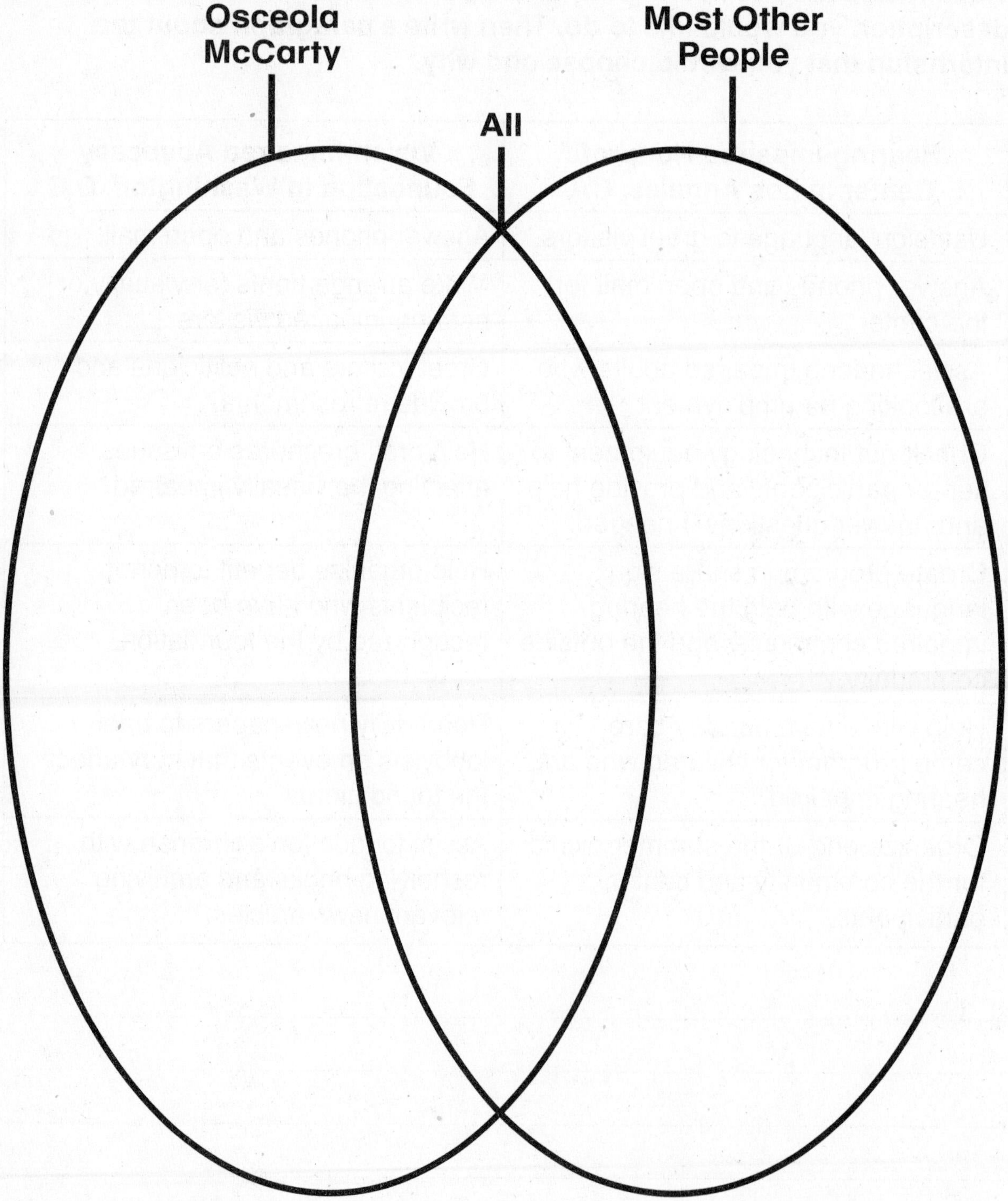

Osceola McCarty

All

Most Other People

How does the information you wrote in this Venn Diagram help you monitor comprehension of *Saving Grace*?

At Home: Have the student use the chart to retell the story.

Name ______________________________

As I read, I will pay attention to tempo or expression.

Annie Dodge, who was born in 1910, grew up on her father's ranch, in
13 New Mexico. Relatives lived nearby and visited often.
21 Around age five, Annie Dodge began tending her father's sheep. Sheep
32 are important to Navajo life. Annie's father raised them for wool and meat.
45 Each day Annie made sure they had grass to eat and water to drink, and
60 each night she locked them into the safety of their corrals. Then she helped
74 each spring at lambing time, and Chee Dodge gave her a lamb or two so
89 she could build up a flock of her own.
98 However for the first eight months of Annie's life, she did not live with her
113 father. She lived in a hogan. The hogan had one room with a central fire and
129 a dirt floor. It did not have electricity or running water. But then her
143 father, Chee Dodge took Annie to live with him.
152 Because she lived with her father, Annie's life was different from other
164 Navajo children. Annie grew up in a large home with many rooms and wood
178 floors. Her father was wealthy as well as powerful. He had two ranches.
191 He owned thousands of sheep, cattle, and horses. However, Annie never
202 forgot that she had begun her life in a hogan, and that she should help
217 those less fortunate. 220

Comprehension Check

1. How was Annie's life similar to other Navajos? How was her life different? **Compare and Contrast**

2. What clues indicate that Annie was very responsible? **Make Inferences**

	Words Read	–	Number of Errors	=	Words Correct Score
First Read		–		=	
Second Read		–		=	

At Home: Help the student read the passage, paying attention to the goal at the top of the page.

Name ____________________

The **parts of a book** can help you quickly find and identify information. The **title page** and **copyright page** have information about the title, book, author, publisher, copyright, and key words. The **table of contents** list the chapter titles with corresponding page numbers. A **glossary** defines unfamiliar words. An **index** is an alphabetical list of different topics with a range of page numbers.

You have just written your first book about a famous entrepreneur who left his successful business to work with young people to promote fitness and exercise. In his daily life, Miguel is a coach and teacher at the local high school. In his free time, he goes canoeing and kayaking. Miguel has also participated in marathons in many states to raise awareness about heart disease.

Use the information provided to answer the questions below.

1. Write three fictional chapter titles that could describe Miguel's early life.

____

____

____

2. Miguel was asked to carry a sporting event's torch from Miami to Jacksonville. Where would you place a reference for this event?

____

3. Where could you place information about unfamiliar running terms?

____

4. Which key words could be listed on the copyright page and in a card catalog? ____________________

____

At Home: Together, look at a few books and identify the different parts that make up each book.

Name ______________________________

Homographs are words that share the same spelling, but have different definitions. Some homographs have different pronounciations.

For each homograph below, write two pronunciations and then write a sentence to show the meaning of each pronunciation. Use a dictionary to check the pronunciations.

close

1. ____________ ______________________________
____

2. ____________ ______________________________
____

content

3. ____________ ______________________________
____

4. ____________ ______________________________
____

minute

5. ____________ ______________________________
____

6. ____________ ______________________________
____

present

7. ____________ ______________________________
____

8. ____________ ______________________________
____

At Home: Together, brainstorm other words that have the same spellings but different pronunciations and meanings.

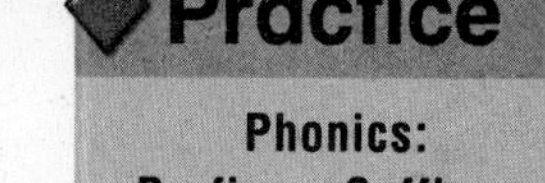

Name ____________________

You can often use what you know about **prefixes**, **suffixes**, and **base words** to figure out the meaning of a new word.

A. Read each word below. Underline the prefix with a single line, double-underline the suffix, and circle the base word. Then write the meaning of each word on the line following it.

1. discourteously ____________________
2. inadequately ____________________
3. illegally ____________________
4. mismanagement ____________________
5. unreasonableness ____________________
6. outrageous ____________________

B. Use each of the words above in a sentence of your own.

7. ____________________
8. ____________________
9. ____________________
10. ____________________
11. ____________________
12. ____________________

At Home: Have the student name words that are related to the base words above but have different prefixes and/or suffixes.

Name ____________________

Write an announcement about famous cyclist, Jahlani Johnson, who is returning from a successful bike racing schedule in Europe. Use the following vocabulary words in your announcement and mention that he will sign autographs.

adept	collective	demonstration	luxury
maneuvered	prevail	prominent	spectators

Name ______________________________

Read the passage and answer the questions.

Bicycles come in all shapes and sizes. They provide people with the opportunity to exercise, and they offer an environmentally friendly means of transportation. Before you purchase a bicycle, you should consider how you will use it and where you will ride it. Racing bicycles are made for speed. They have light frames and thin tires. Mountain bikes, on the other hand, are built to travel over rugged terrain. They have sturdy frames and thick tires with deep treads. The best bike for city riding is the hybrid. It combines elements of a racing bike and a mountain bike. Hybrids are light enough to carry up stairs, and their tires are thick enough to withstand potholes. However, they are thin enough to gather speed. Whichever bike you choose, you have made a good decision to ride!

1. Racing bicycles are made for speed. Fact or opinion? ____________
2. What opinion does the author offer about one of the bikes?

   ____

3. What opinion does the author give about bike riding in general?

   ____

   ____

4. What facts does the author give about mountain bikes?

   ____

   ____

5. What facts does the author give about hybrid bikes?

   ____

   ____

   ____

6. Where could you check the facts that are presented in this passage?

   ____

   ____

At Home: Have the student tell his or her opinion about a topic that interests you both.

Name ______________________________

As you read *Major Taylor,* fill in the Fact and Opinion Chart.

Fact	Opinion

How does the information you wrote in this Fact and Opinion Chart help you monitor comprehension of *Major Taylor*?

At Home: Have the student use the chart to retell the story.

Name ____

As I read, I will pay attention to tempo.

James Cleveland Owens was born in Alabama in 1913. He was the
11 son of a sharecropper. J.C. was a frail child who was often ill. By the
26 time he was eight, his family moved to Cleveland, Ohio. His father
38 hoped to find better work there.
44 On the boy's first day at his new school, his teacher asked his name.
58 He replied "J.C." The teacher misunderstood him and thought he said
69 "*Jesse*." He was called Jesse from that day on.
78 Because his family was poor, Jesse worked at a number of jobs. He
91 worked whenever he had time. He took all types of jobs. He delivered
104 groceries, he loaded freight, and he worked in a shoe shop. For fun, he
118 liked to run.
121 One day at school students were timed as they ran a 60-yard dash. The
134 coach, Charlie Riley, noticed Jesse right away. Impressed by Jesse's
144 speed, the coach invited him to join the track team. But Jesse had to
158 decline because of his work. He would not be able to attend the regular
172 after-school practices.
174 Riley made a special offer. He would train Jesse in the mornings so
187 that Jesse could work after school. Jesse agreed. 195

Comprehension Check

1. Why was Riley the first person to notice Jesse's talent? **Make Inferences**

2. Why did the author write about Jesse's background? **Author's Purpose**

	Words Read	–	Number of Errors	=	Words Correct Score
First Read		–		=	
Second Read		–		=	

At Home: Help the student read the passage, paying attention to the goal at the top of the page.

Name ___________________________________

Poetry uses language in special ways.
Assonance is the repetition of the same middle vowel sound in two or more closely grouped words. Examples: *dumpy skunk*, *our flower*, *missed whisk*, *metal pedal*.
Sometimes words that have assonance can rhyme.
Onomatopoeia is the use of a word to sound like or imitate what the word describes. Examples: *rattle*, *click*, *meow*, *whoosh*.

Look at the poem below about riding a bike. Fill in the blanks. Make sure you use words that have assonance or show onomatopoeia. The poem does not have to rhyme.

I pedal through the ________________,

My feet ________________ and ________________,

I ________________ and ________________ up the hill's steep side,

________________ and ________________ down it in full stride,

My coat flaps and ________________ in the breeze,

My gears ________________ and ________________ as I wheeze,

The wind ________________ and ________________ in my ear,

Stop sign! ________________, ________________, I must brake here,

I catch my breath, I wipe my face, I take a break at ________________

________________, ________________, I drink ________________ .

At Home: Brainstorm with the student words that have onomatopoeia such as *buzz, clang,* and *gush.*

Name ______________________________

Analogies can help you identify **relationships** between words. Many analogies show relationships between words that are antonyms or synonyms. Some analogies show relationships between words that demonstrate a part to a whole, a cause to an effect, a degree, or an amount.
For example: game : series :: round : championship
A game is part of a series. A round is part of a championship. The relationship between the pairs of words is part to whole.

Read the first part of each analogy and determine the relationship. Then write two words to complete the analogy. Explain why your words have the same relationship as the given words.

1. pedal : bike :: ______________ : ______________

____

____

2. cyclist : race :: ______________ : ______________

____

____

____

3. snap : photograph :: ______________ : ______________

____

____

4. proprietor : store :: ______________ : ______________

____

____

____

At Home: Have the student write one or two of his or her own analogies.

Name ______________________________

Circle the pair of words in each group that shows vowel alternation when a suffix is added or changed. Underline the vowel(s) that changed and write each word in a sentence.

1. **a.** announce/ announcement **b.** pronounce/ pronunciation **c.** attend/ attentive

____

____

2. **a.** demolish/ demolition **b.** frustrate/ frustration **c.** secret/ secretive

____

____

3. **a.** treasure/ treasury **b.** withdraw/ withdrawal **c.** courage/ courageous

____

____

____

4. **a.** perfect/ perfection **b.** perspire/ perspiration **c.** manage/ manager

____

____

5. **a.** collide/ collision **b.** calculate/ calculation **c.** connect/ connection

____

____

____

At Home: Have the student say words both with and without their suffixes.

Name ______________________________

A. For each vocabulary word below, write three clue words like the example shown below.

pride: ego, arrogance, vanity

1. deftly: ____________ ____________ ____________
2. benefit: ____________ ____________ ____________
3. eaves: ____________ ____________ ____________
4. derision: ____________ ____________ ____________
5. symmetry: ____________ ____________ ____________
6. ceramics: ____________ ____________ ____________
7. furrowed: ____________ ____________ ____________
8. arid: ____________ ____________ ____________

B. In a common word game, one player draws picture clues to help his or her partner guess a given word. Choose one of the vocabulary words from above and draw a picture clue to help your partner guess that word.

Name ______________________________

Write a paragraph about something that happened to you that also involved someone else such as a friend, parent, teacher, teammate, or other person. Write the paragraph the first time from your perspective. Then rewrite the paragraph from the other person's perspective.

From my perspective: ______________________________

____

____

____

____

____

____

____

____

____

From: ______________________________

____

____

____

____

____

____

____

____

____

____

____

At Home: Together, discuss something that happened to both of you.

Name ______________________________

As you read *A Single Shard,* fill in the Character Web.

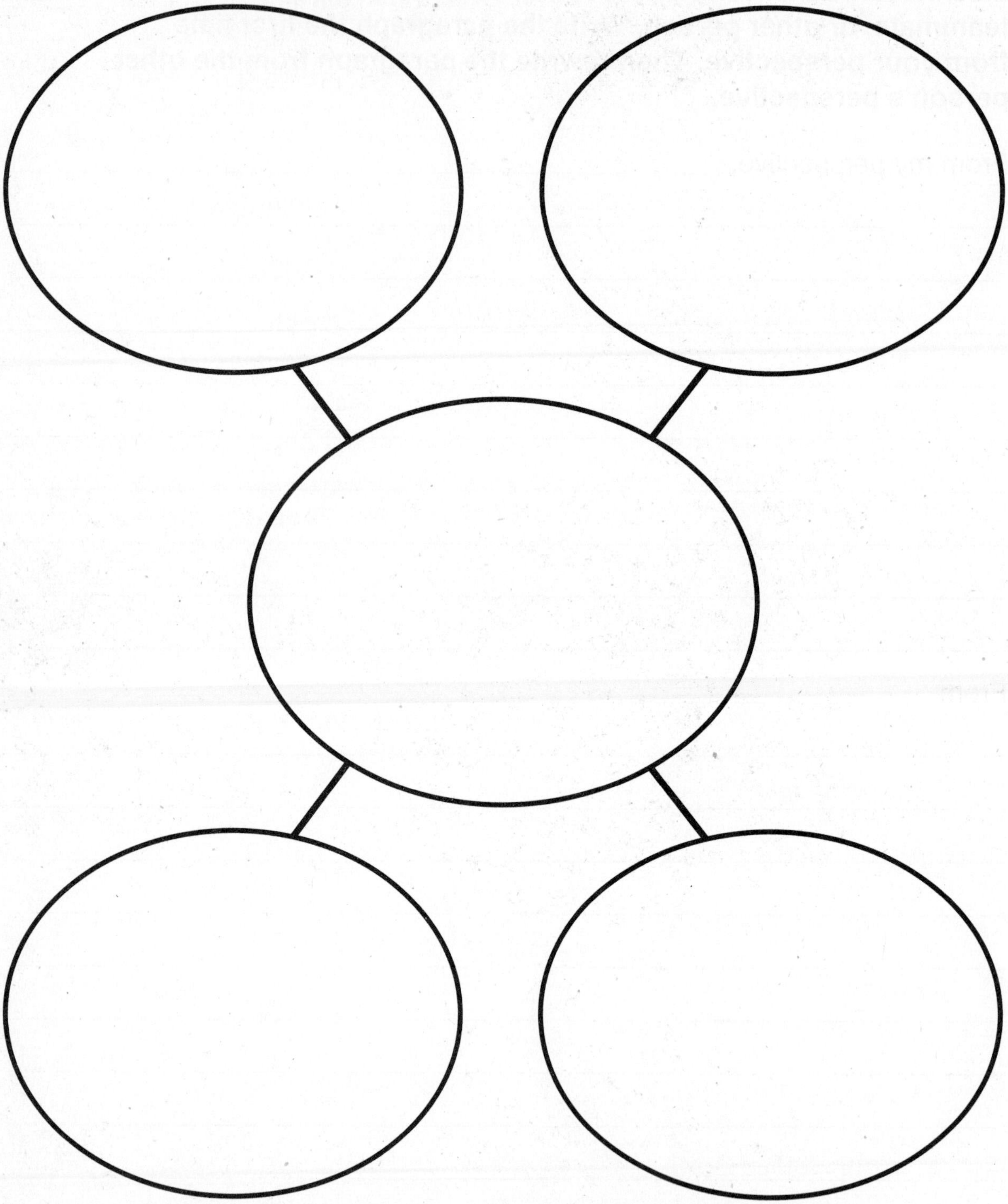

How does the information you wrote in the Author's Perspective Web help you monitor comprehension of *A Single Shard*?

At Home: Have the student use the chart to retell the story.

Name ______________________________

As I read, I will pay attention to pauses and intonation.

For medieval people, a church was much more than a building
11 where they went to hear Mass and say prayers. For many people,
23 it opened up a new and wonderful world. It gave them hope.
35 People came from their crowded, smoky cottages into a world of
46 glowing colors and rich tapestries. The rich decorations in a church
57 might be the only beautiful art a medieval peasant would see in his
70 or her lifetime.
73 The church was also a center for the community. People flocked
84 there on the eves of holidays. They crowded into the church in times
97 of war and went there to be married, and at other important times.
110 The largest and most important church in an area was the cathedral.
122 A high-ranking priest called a bishop headed it. Bishops often became
133 wealthy. One way to show off their wealth and power was to build a
147 beautiful new cathedral. Rulers and nobles also gave gold to fund
158 the building of a cathedral. Kings and nobles believed that their gifts
170 to the Church were a good way of showing their respect.
181 Sometimes entire cities and towns helped to build a cathedral. A
192 cathedral would bring their town fame and prestige. A number of
203 medieval cities even competed to build the biggest one. 212

Comprehension Check

1. Find at least five words in the passage that are homophones. List them along with their homophones. **Homophones**

2. Why did the author write about the role the church played in the lives of medieval people? **Author's Purpose**

	Words Read	–	Number of Errors	=	Words Correct Score
First Read		–		=	
Second Read		–		=	

At Home: Help the student read the passage, paying attention to the goal at the top of the page.

Name ______________________________________

Articles and entries in encyclopedias and other references, such as textbooks, often use different **typefaces** and sizes to highlight important parts of the text.
The **topic** of the entry is usually bold and in a larger size than the rest of the text.
Words that are important are often in bold or in a color that sets them off from the text.
Other topics that relate to the entry, called cross-references, are all in CAPITALS.
Below is an encyclopedia entry about Korean pottery.

Use what you know about typefaces to mark the sample encyclopedia entry below. Circle words that should be boldfaced. Underline words that should be larger than the regular text. If you want to use capital letters, underline those words, parts, or letters with three lines.

Korean Pottery

The Chinese influenced the style, form, glazing methods, and brush techniques of Korean pottery for centuries. Korean merchants and traders to China probably brought back the first examples of Chinese pottery and clay. Koreans may have even traveled to China to learn the art of making pottery. During the Three Kingdoms period, 57 b.c. to a.d. 668, Korean potters produced plain pottery for ordinary people and very elaborate statues as burial artifacts. The methods used to make these ceramic funeral objects included the ancient methods of coiling and hammering clay, as well as potter's wheels. Scholars have compared the Korean Three Kingdoms pottery to the Han Dynasty pottery of China.

At Home: Name some topics and have the student tell where in the encyclopedia he or she would find that topic.

Name ______________________________

A. Write the homophone(s) of the word on the line.

1. so ____________

2. in ____________

3. wood ____________

4. for ____________

5. where ____________

6. no ____________

7. night ____________

8. him ____________

9. all ____________

10. there ____________

11. not ____________

12. be ____________

13. bore ____________

14. new ____________

15. I ____________

16. one ____________

17. past ____________

18. to ____________

19. sell ____________

20. by ____________

B. Choose five pairs of homophones from the list and write a sentence for each pair. Underline the homophones you use.

21. ______________________________

____

22. ______________________________

____

23. ______________________________

____

24. ______________________________

____

25. ______________________________

____

At Home: Brainstorm with the student other homophones that you both know.

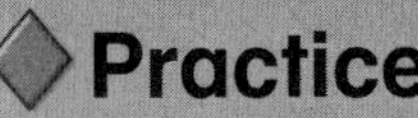

Name ______________________

Practice

Phonics: Consonant Alternation

Write each base word with a suffix so that the final consonant sound of the base word changes. Then write each base word with its suffix in the chart below to show how the consonant sound changed. Use a dictionary as needed.

1. discuss ______________
2. act ______________
3. office ______________
4. critic ______________
5. public ______________
6. impress ______________
7. destruct ______________
8. romantic ______________
9. project ______________
10. express ______________
11. connect ______________
12. music ______________

/k/ to /s/	/k/ to /sh/	/s/ to /sh/	/t/ to /sh/
______	______	______	______
______	______	______	______
______	______	______	______
______	______	______	______
______	______	______	______

At Home: Together, use the word lists above to generalize rules about when final consonants might change if suffixes are added.

Name ______________________________

A. Write a paragraph using these vocabulary words.

adept	specialists	guidance	moderate
prominent	intact	severed	symmetry

____

____

____

____

____

____

____

____

B. Write a context clue for the underlined vocabulary words.

1. Vijay was discouraged by the <u>bewildering</u> and ______________ rules.
2. Natalie set up a <u>demonstration</u> to ______________ the new product.
3. The wealthy Plumptons had every <u>benefit</u> and ______________ at their disposal.
4. Every decision had to be approved by the <u>collective</u> or ______________.
5. She could see the players using her <u>peripheral</u> ______________ vision.
6. Fatima <u>maneuvered</u> the soccer ball in a ______________ move through the other team's defense.

Name ______________________________

Use the clues to solve the crossword puzzle below.

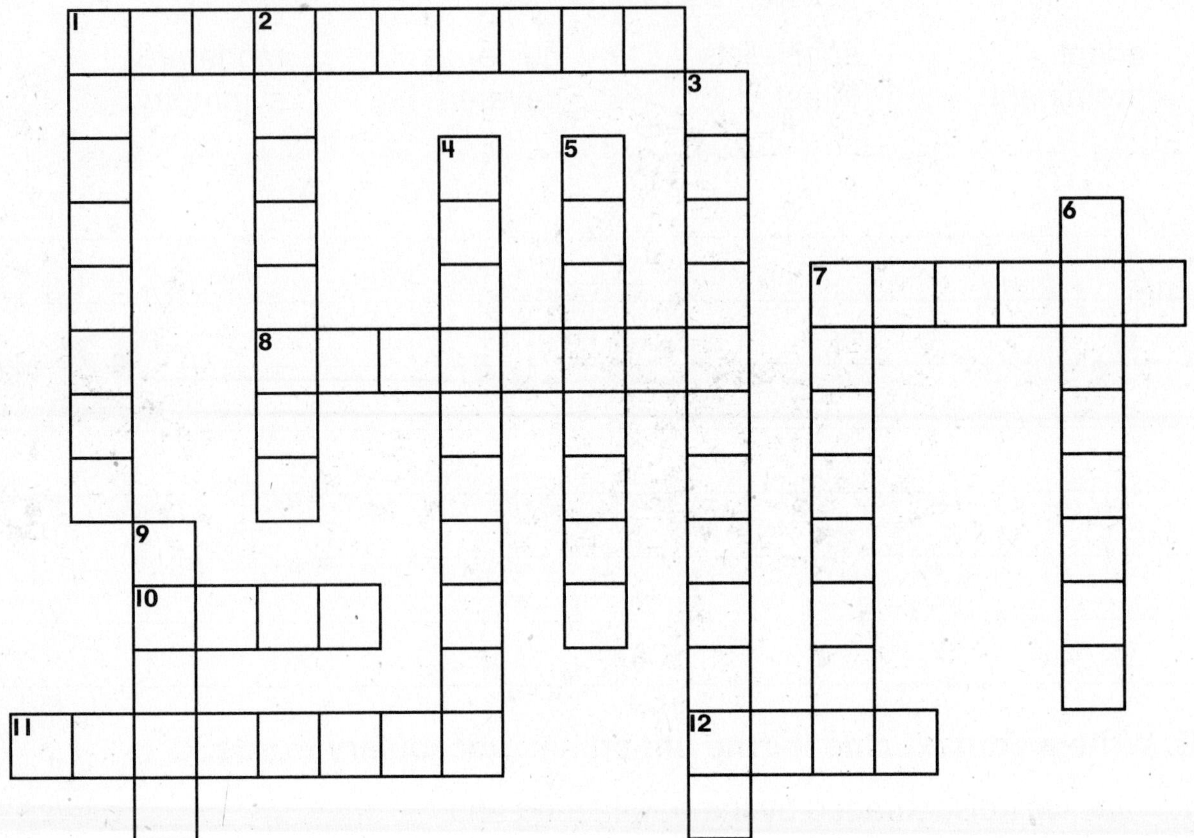

Across

1. something that is formed
7. impede or interfere
8. the inside part
10. desiccated, lifeless
11. leftover destruction
12. impatient

Down

1. creased
2. full physical and mental development
3. became worse
4. easy to get at
5. scorn
6. pottery
7. staying in one place in the air
9. the overhanging part of a roof

Name ______________________________

A. Write a word to complete each analogy. Use a dictionary or thesaurus if needed.

1. weak : frail :: ruptured : ______________
2. moaned : complained :: uttered : ______________
3. failed : succeeded :: mistreated : ______________
4. fixed : corrected :: migrant : ______________
5. history : chronology :: reputation : ______________
6. frightened : soothed :: quickened : ______________
7. advance : progress :: wrath : ______________
8. exhausted : rested :: illegally : ______________

B. Write a sentence that includes both given vocabulary words.

9. ruptured, reputation ______________________________

____

10. mistreated, illegally ______________________________

____

____

11. migrant, wrath ______________________________

____

12. uttered, quickened ______________________________

____

Name ____

Write a letter to an author whose work you really like. In your letter tell the author what you liked best about his or her writing. Suggest other ideas for books that this author might write. The book ideas that you suggest, along with the work you really like, should cover the main author's purposes: to inform, to entertain, or to persuade.

At Home: Discuss with the student the author's purpose in various writing that you encounter in your daily lives.

Name ______________________________

As you read *Breaking Through,* fill in the Author's Purpose Chart.

Clues	Author's Purpose

How does the information you wrote in this Author's Purpose Chart help you monitor comprehension of *Breaking Through*?

At Home: Have the student use the chart to retell the story.

Name ______________________________

As I read, I will pay attention to pauses, stops, and intonation.

Pedro sat in his social studies class and watched as the wind swept
13 through the courtyard, carrying away the last of the autumn leaves. He
25 noticed a flock of **migrant** birds flying in the distance, on their way to the
40 warm tropics. Pedro knew winter was coming.
47 Suddenly, his thoughts were interrupted by the sound of his teacher
58 entering the classroom. Mrs. Petrovski had the **reputation** of being the
69 best teacher in school. All of the students liked her because she made
82 even the most boring lessons fun, and because she took her students on
95 more field trips than anyone else. She was the most enthusiastic teacher
107 Pedro had ever met.
111 That morning, Mrs. Petrovski looked very excited. The students sat in
122 silence as Mrs. Petrovski walked to the blackboard and without **uttering** a
134 word, wrote "Oral History."
138 Joseph was first to break the silence and asked, "What is oral history,
151 anyway?"
152 Mrs. Petrovski explained that before the invention of books, people
162 passed information from generation to generation through stories. She
171 told the class that oral history was still very important even though
183 information was now available in books and on the Internet.
193 "I bet all of you know at least one person who tells interesting stories,"
207 Mrs. Petrovski said. "That is why we are going to record our oral
220 history!" 221

Comprehension Check

1. What do you think the author's purpose is? **Author's Purpose**

2. What do you think happens if oral history is not recorded? **Draw Conclusions**

	Words Read	–	Number of Errors	=	Words Correct Score
First Read		–		=	
Second Read		–		=	

At Home: Help the student read the passage paying attention to the goal at the top of the page

Name ____________________

A. Suppose you volunteer to mentor Francisco, the student whose schedule is shown below. Your schedule follows. Identify at least two blocks of time each week when you and Francisco could meet. Circle the times on the schedule.

Francisco's Afternoon Schedule

Time	Monday	Tuesday	Wednesday	Thursday	Friday
12:00–12:30	Spanish	Lunch	Spanish	Lunch	Spanish
12:30–1:30	Social Studies	Social Studies	Social Studies	Social Studies	Social Studies
1:30–2:30	Science	Science	Science	Science	Science
2:30–3:00	Drama Club	Band	Study	Study	Band
3:00–5:00		Work at school			Work at school

Mentor's Afternoon Schedule

Time	Monday	Tuesday	Wednesday	Thursday	Friday
12:00–12:30	Lunch	Lunch	Lunch	Lunch	Lunch
12:30–1:30	Spanish	Spanish	PE	PE	Spanish
1:30–2:30	Social Studies	Social Studies	Science	Science	Science
2:30–3:00	Study	Basketball Practice	Basketball Practice	Study	Basketball Practice
3:00–5:00		Basketball Practice	Basketball Game		

B. Write a paragraph explaining the blocks of time when you and Francisco could meet.

____

____

____

____

____

____

____

At Home: Have the student show you his or her schedule and ask him or her questions about it.

Name ______________________________

For each word given below, write as many related words for the word family as you can. Adding inflectional endings *(s, -ed, -ing)* to a word does not count. Use a dictionary if needed.

1. shiny ______________________________

2. really ______________________________

3. correction ______________________________

4. disappoint ______________________________

5. memorize ______________________________

6. experience ______________________________

7. assignment ______________________________

8. succeed ______________________________

9. stick ______________________________

10. light ______________________________

At Home: Together, review the list of words that the student wrote. Add more words if possible.

Name ______________________________

For each given homophone, write the word or words that have the same sound but a different spelling. Then, use each word in a sentence.

1. a. find ______________________________

____

b. __________ ______________________________

____

2. a. navel ______________________________

____

b. __________ ______________________________

____

3. a. groan ______________________________

____

b. __________ ______________________________

____

4. a. aloud ______________________________

____

b. __________ ______________________________

____

5. a. missed ______________________________

____

b. __________ ______________________________

____

6. a. due ______________________________

b. __________ ______________________________

c. __________ ______________________________

At Home: Together, brainstorm other homophones that you each know. Have the student tell you the meanings and spelling of each.

Name ______________________________

For each vocabulary word, write one true statement or one false statement. Write T or F in parentheses after each sentence.

1. encounter

____

2. victorious

____

3. grimaced

____

4. participate

____

5. ordeals

____

6. nourishing

____

7. anticipated

____

8. dejectedly

____

Name ______________________________

Use the information in the chart to write an essay comparing and contrasting the two people and how they solve problems.

The Ways Marty and Mary Solve Problems

Marty	Both	Mary
focuses on a single solution	smart	brainstorms many possible solutions
very cautious—thinks through all steps before beginning work	reliable	jumps right in and impulsively starts working
sometimes has to start over because his solution does not work	patient	sometimes has to backtrack to fix mistakes

Now use the chart to write a comparison-contrast essay.

____

____

____

____

____

____

____

____

____

____

____

____

At Home: Have the student compare and contrast him- or herself with a good friend.

Name ______________________________

As you read *Ta-Na-E-Ka,* fill in the Venn Diagram.

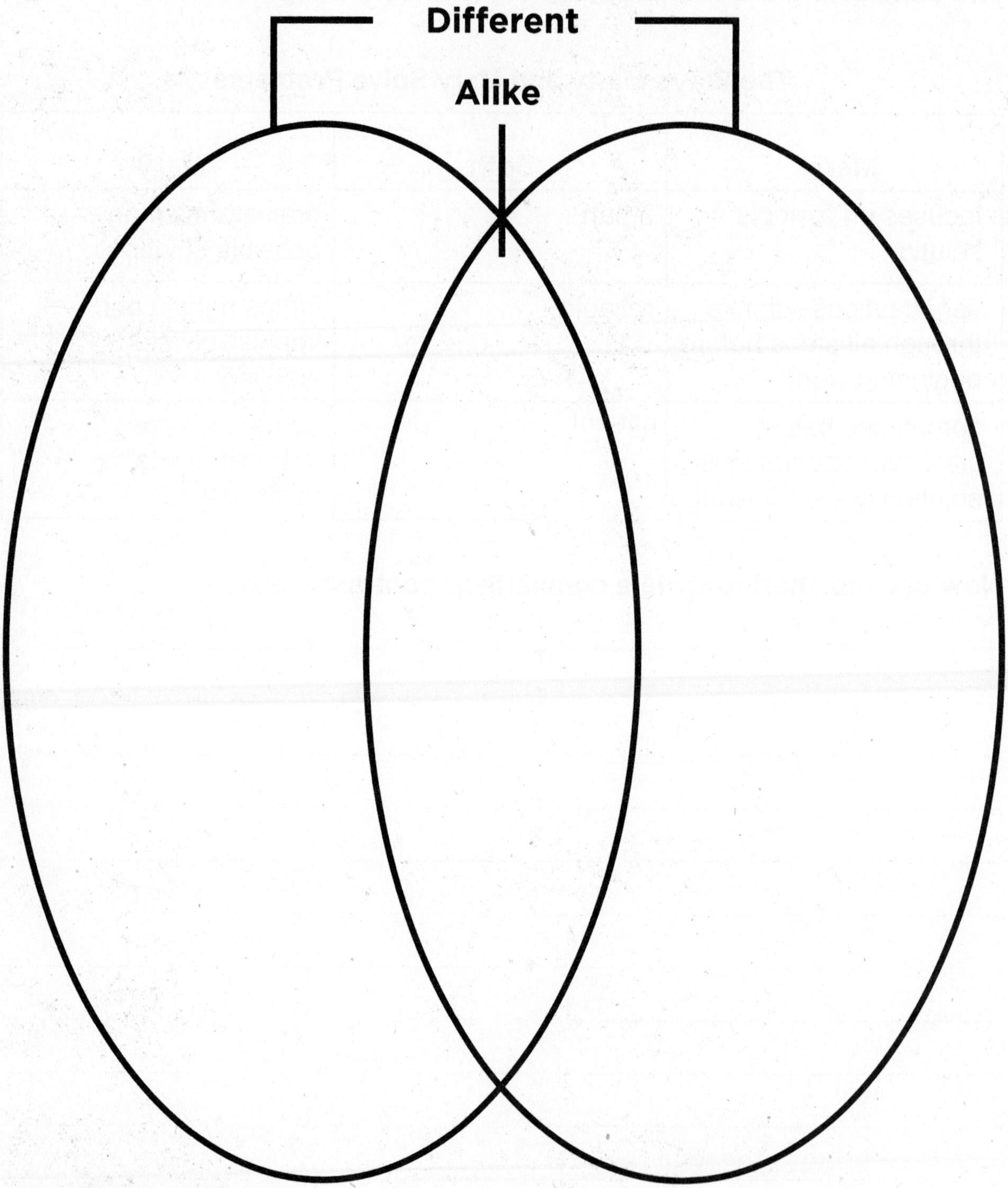

Different

Alike

How does the information you wrote in this Venn Diagram help you monitor comprehension of *Ta-Na-E-Ka*?

At Home: Have the student use the chart to retell the story.

Name ______________________________

As I read, I will pay attention to punctuation and characters' voices.

The sound of tires crunching on the gravel driveway told her that her
13 mom was home. Anna dropped the pail and ran around to the front yard to
28 greet her. "Hey, Mom!" she yelled. "How come you're so la—" She stopped
41 short. Her mom had a long scratch on her face, and her left arm was in a
58 sling. "Are you okay? What happened?"
64 Mrs. Willard shook her head, grimacing. "I was showing a young couple
76 that old farm way out on Sugar Hollow Road, and like a fool I tried to climb
93 the ladder in the barn and fell."
100 Anna looked at her mom, who was wearing her usual suit and heels—
113 reasonable clothes for a real estate agent, but not for climbing rickety
125 old ladders.
127 "I should have known better than to go anywhere near a farm," her mom
141 **grimaced** in pain and went on disgustedly. "As far as I'm concerned, nothing
154 good could ever happen there."
159 Ordinarily, Anna would have protested indignantly. Her favorite place in
169 the world was the family farm where her mom and Aunt Rachel had grown
183 up. Almost every morning she rode her bicycle a mile and a half each way
198 to help milk the cows and tend the chickens. Her three cousins, Brady, Pete,
212 and Eddie, groaned about their chores, but Anna thought the work was
224 fun. 225

Comprehension Check

1. Compare and contrast Mrs. Willard's opinion about farms and Anna's opinion. **Compare and Contrast**

2. Why do you think Anna does not protest her mom's opinion? **Author's Perspective**

	Words Read	–	Number of Errors	=	Words Correct Score
First Read		–		=	

At Home: Help the student read the passage, paying attention to the goal at the top of the page

Name ________________________________

Read Aesop's fable, *Belling the Cat.* Explain how this story fits into the fable genre and give examples of its characteristics such as personification and moral.

Belling the Cat

Cat was prowling around looking for mice to eat. This cat was a good hunter, and bit-by-bit the mouse population was shrinking. The mice knew that they had to do something to stop the cat. So the elders of the mouse community called a great meeting to come up with a plan for dealing with Cat.

Mice came from all over to attend the meeting. Everyone was excitedly chattering about the cat, but no one had any solutions to offer. Finally, after everyone else had spoken, the youngest mouse at the meeting asked to be heard. He said that he had been listening to all the discussion and that everyone seemed to agree on one thing—Cat was very sly and quiet. The mouse proposed putting a bell around the cat's neck so that they could hear it coming and have time to scamper away.

Great cheers broke out among the crowd. Some mice believed that the young mouse had solved their problem. Then they saw the council's oldest mouse trying to get their attention. When the room was quiet, the oldest mouse said, "Belling the cat will certainly let us know when the cat approaches, but which of you will volunteer to tie a bell around the cat's neck?" When no volunteers stepped forward, the oldest mouse added, "It's easy to propose impossible solutions to problems."

____

____

____

____

____

____

____

____

At Home: Discuss other fables with which you and the student are familiar.

Name ______________________________

Write a story about a mentor and a student. In your story, use at least ten of these or other words that have the Latin roots *ject, spect*, *dura* and *liber*. Underline each word you use that has one of these Latin roots.

Latin Root	Meaning	Examples
ject	throw	conjecture, dejectedly, eject, inject, project, reject, subject
spect	see	expect, inspect, respect, spectacle, spectacular, spectator, speculate, suspect
dura	last	durable, duration, during, endurance
liber	free	liberal, liberate, liberation, liberty

At Home: Discuss with the student how identifying a Latin root and knowing its meaning can help a reader figure out an unknown word.

Name ______________________________

Combine the following prefixes, roots, and suffixes to make words that match the meanings given. Then write a form of each word in a sentence. Use a dictionary if needed.

Prefixes and Meanings		Latin Roots and Meanings		Suffixes and Meanings	
ex-	out of	*port*	carry	-able	able to
in-	into	*scrib*	write	-ion	the act of
post-	after	*spect*	see	-or	one who or that which
trans-	across	*tract*	pull or drag		

1. one who sees ____________ ____________________
____
2. to write by carving into ____________ ____________________
____
3. to carry across ____________ ____________________
____
4. to look into carefully ____________ ____________________
____
5. that which pulls ____________ ____________________
____
6. the act of pulling ____________ ____________________
____
7. to carry out of ____________ ____________________
____
8. able to be carried ____________ ____________________
____

At Home: Together, combine other prefixes, roots, and/or suffixes to make other words that you know.

Name ______________________

Fill in the blanks to finish the multiple-choice test for these vocabulary words. Then circle the correct answer.

chronology	continuous	debut	economists	periodic

1. Which word is a synonym for ________________?
   a. completed
   b. continent
   c. opposing
   d. ongoing

2. Which word is an antonym for ________________?
   a. start
   b. constant
   c. end
   d. yearly

3. Which word is an example of ________________?
   a. a photograph
   b. a map
   c. a timeline
   d. a diagram

4. Which word means ________________?
   a. introduction
   b. greeting
   c. handshake
   d. farewell

5. Which word **best** completes this sentence?

   It is the job of ________________ to understand how people use money, goods, and services.
   a. chronology
   b. continuous
   c. economists
   d. periodic

Name ___________________________

Write the framework for a persuasive essay about why people should save their money. Use the questions below to see what you must include in your framework.

1. What sentence will you use to introduce your topic? ______________

____

____

2. What three logical arguments will you offer the reader?

a. ____

____

____

b. ____

____

____

c. ____

____

____

3. What persuasive words did you use in your arguments? ______________

____

4. With what strong ending argument will you close? ______________

____

____

____

At Home: Have the student write a paragraph telling why he or she is easily persuaded and why.

Name ____

As you read *Many Countries, One Currency*, fill in the Persuasion Chart.

Word or phrase	Kind of persuasion

How does the information you wrote in this Persuasion Chart help you monitor comprehension of *Many Countries, One Currency*?

At Home: Have the student use the chart to retell the story.

Name ____________________

As I read, I will pay attention to the pronunciation of vocabulary and other difficult words.

The decade of the 1920s is known as the Roaring '20s. After World War I,
12 the country went on a spending spree. For many Americans, life turned
25 into an almost ten-year-long party. One cause for celebration was the
36 economy. For a few years just before and during World War I, Americans
48 didn't spend much money. Industries were producing more weapons and war
59 goods than things for consumers to buy. After the war, people were eager
72 to buy new things. Corporations were eager to sell goods. Our economy
84 boomed. Some **economists** warned that the boom couldn't last forever, but
95 people felt confident in the future and ready to enjoy themselves.
106 The 1920s were a time when technology changed American life. Henry
116 Ford made the Model-T. He used an assembly line and produced a large
129 number of cars. The mass production of cars lowered the price of a car. Now
144 the average American family could afford a car. Soon families began to drive
157 and take vacations. They spent money at motels and restaurants.
167 New appliances such as refrigerators and washing machines also changed
177 the lives of millions of Americans. These appliances gave people more free
189 time. People bought all these new things. But they often spent money they
202 didn't have. 204

Comprehension Check

1. How did technology make more free time for people? **Make Inferences**

2. What opinion did many people have about the future? What was one fact many overlooked? **Fact and Opinion**

	Words Read	–	Number of Errors	=	Words Correct Score
First Read		–		=	
Second Read		–		=	

At Home: Help the student read the passage, paying attention to the goal at the top of the page

Name ______________________________

Look up each word in a dictionary and a thesaurus. Write the part of speech and two meanings of each word. Write at least two synonyms of each word.

1. interest __________

____

____

____

Synonyms: ______________________________

2. economy __________

____

____

Synonyms: ______________________________

____

3. bill __________

____

____

Synonyms: ______________________________

Now write a paragraph about spending money carefully that uses the definitions and synonyms for each boldfaced word.

____

____

____

____

____

____

____

At Home: Discuss with the student how a dictionary and a thesaurus are the same and different.

Name ____

Use the clues and base words to determine the correct Greek root. Write the root in the blank.

1. written record of one's own life: ___________ biography

2. top layer of a person's skin: ___________ is

3. involving chemical reactions in living organisms: ___________ chemical

4. ordered sequence of dates and events: ___________ ology

5. coded message sent over telegraph wires: ___________ gram

6. something that moves or acts by itself: ___________ matic

7. image taken by a camera photo: ___________

8. person's initials stitched on fabric mono: ___________

9. group of signs and symptoms that occur together and characterize an illness: ___________ drome

10. word that uses the Greek root for "life" and describes the study of life processes: ___________ logy

11. move forward, advance: ___________ mote

12. put off until the future: ___________ crastinate

At Home: Together, brainstorm other words you know that have the Greek roots *auto*, *derm*, *bio*, *graph*, *gram*, and *chron*.

Name ______________________________

A. Write the letter of the pronunciation that matches each word that has a Greek root.

1. thermometer ____ **a.** tel´ ə fō´ tō
2. photosynthesis ____ **b.** kron´ ik
3. telephoto ____ **c.** krə nol´ ə jē
4. chronology ____ **d.** fō´ tə graf
5. thermostat ____ **e.** ther´ mə stat
6. chronic ____ **f.** ther´ məl
7. photograph ____ **g.** fō´ tə sin´ thə sis
8. thermal ____ **h.** thər mom´ ə tər

B. Use six of the words from above in sentences of your own.

9. thermometer ______________________________

____

10. photosynthesis ______________________________

____

11. telephoto ______________________________

____

12. chronology ______________________________

____

13. thermostat ______________________________

____

14. chronic ______________________________

____

At Home: Have the student identify the Greek root or roots in each word listed at the top of the page.

Name ______________________________

Use each vocabulary word in a story about finding something surprising while cleaning out the attic.

auction	decades	decrease	dilapidated
instinctively	rafters	shakily	swiveled

It was hot as I worked under the dusty attic ________________ cleaning out ________________ of old paper, clothes, books, and assorted other junk. I was moving a pile of ________________ boxes toward the stairs when I caught sight of some movement out of the corner of my eye. ________________ I lowered the boxes to the floor and ________________ my head to see what was behind me. I didn't see anything, so my heart rate started to ________________. I figured I was just spooked by being in such a creaky place for so long. But when I finally started moving again, I caught another flash of movement over in the corner behind a tall stack of boxes. ________________ I crouched down and looked along the floor for movement, but I didn't see anything moving. I stayed crouched like that for a minute, but then I stood up. Again, some movement startled me, but as I stared into the corner I realized what I had seen. One by one I removed the boxes in the corner to reveal a full-length mirror in a delicately carved wooden frame. I'd seen one like this at an ________________ that my grandmother had taken me to. I wondered if my mother even remembered that it was up here in Grandma's attic.

Name ______________________________

Read the scenarios below. Write arguments and a judgment for each scenario provided.

1. You have a full-time job, you attend school part-time, and you volunteer as a mentor to a young friend. Your aunt invites you to go to dinner on a night that you volunteer. You haven't seen her in a few months because you are busy. Make a judgment about what you should do.

Argument for: ______________________________

____

Argument against: ______________________________

Make judgment: ______________________________

____

____

____

2. You can pick a team to do a class project. Your friend doesn't understand the material as well as you do. The project takes a lot of research because the material is complex. There are other students in the class who do understand the material. Make a judgment about what you should do.

Argument for: ______________________________

Argument against: ______________________________

____

Make judgment: ______________________________

____

____

____

____

At Home: Discuss with the student judgments you each have made and whether you think they were good or bad judgments.

Name ______________________________

As you read *Honus and Me,* fill in the Make Judgments Chart.

Action	Judgment

How does the information you wrote in this Make Judgments Chart help you monitor comprehension of *Honus and Me*?

At Home: Have the student use the chart to retell the story.

Name ______________________________

As I read, I will pay attention to tempo.

Where can you find a set from a famous television show and a $20
13 million portrait of George Washington? The Smithsonian Institution, of course!
23 Those are just two of the millions of items in the Smithsonian. Some people
37 call the Smithsonian America's attic. It has everything you might store in an
50 attic—and a whole lot more. The number of items in the collections will
64 never **decrease**. It just grows larger.
70 Why do people collect? Some want pretty things to look at or hope their
84 collection will increase in value over the years. Others collect to remember
96 the past. The Smithsonian collects things that tell America's stories.
106 People from all over the world visit the Smithsonian. They come to see
119 the Hope Diamond, the Wright brothers' airplane, and the ruby slippers from
131 The Wizard of Oz. Today the Smithsonian is a group of 17 museums and 9
144 research centers. It is the largest complex of museums in the world.
156 The Smithsonian began with a single bequest from a man
166 who donated money. It has grown into one of the world's most important
179 centers for storing knowledge. Objects have come to the Smithsonian in
190 many ways. People donate items that are precious to them. The museum
202 buys others or gets them at **auctions**. And sometimes curators go out
214 scavenging. 215

Comprehension Check

1. Why do you think the Smithsonian is important? **Make Judgments**

2. Why do you think the Smithsonian draws people from all over the world? **Draw Conclusions**

	Words Read	–	Number of Errors	=	Words Correct Score
First Read		–		=	
Second Read		–		=	

At Home: Help the student read the passage, paying attention to the goal at the top of the page.

Name ______________________________

What if you were working on a photo essay about collections? Plan five photographs. Describe what you want each photograph to show and then write a caption for each.

1. Photograph: ______________________________
____
Caption: ______________________________
____

2. Photograph: ______________________________
____
Caption: ______________________________
____

3. Photograph: ______________________________
____
Caption: ______________________________
____

4. Photograph: ______________________________
____
Caption: ______________________________
____

5. Photograph: ______________________________
____
Caption: ______________________________
____
____

At Home: Have the student look at photographs and write his or her own captions for them.

Name ______________________________

For each of the five types of antonyms, an example is given. Write two more examples of antonyms for each type. Use a thesaurus or dictionary.

Contradictory antonyms are those that have no "in-between-ness." For example, *dead* and *alive.*

1. ________________ ________________

2. ________________ ________________

Contrary antonyms are those opposite concepts that do have some "in-between-ness." For example, *beautiful* and *ugly* are opposites but between those extremes are other opposites such as *pretty, attractive,* and *plain.*

3. ________________ ________________

4. ________________ ________________

Relative-pair antonyms are those that show a reversal of meaning. For example, *mother* and *father.*

5. ________________ ________________

6. ________________ ________________

Complementary antonyms are those words for which you expect another related but opposite response. For example, *question* and *answer* are complementary antonyms.

7. ________________ ________________

8. ________________ ________________

Contrasted antonyms are those that are not the total opposites of one another because they can be partly like each other. For example, *cloudy* and *sunny* are contrasting antonyms.

9. ________________ ________________

10. ________________ ________________

At Home: With the student brainstorm other examples of antonyms and determine the category for each.

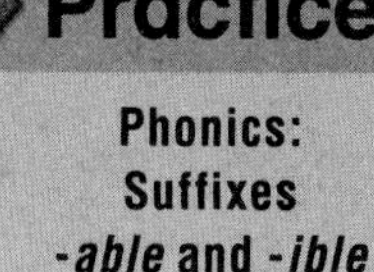

Name ______________________________

Remember that the suffixes ***-able*** and ***-ible*** both mean "able or likely." In general, you use *-able* when you attach the suffix to a base word and *-ible* when you attach it to a word root.
Decide whether to drop the silent *e* at the end of a word when you add *-able.* Look at these two examples: manageable and desirable. When the base word ends in a soft /g/ or /c/ sound, you keep the silent *e* when you add the *-able* ending and you drop it in other cases.

Decide which suffix to use with each word or word root. Write the complete word in the correct part of the chart below. Number the words you place in the chart.

1. understand	**6.** knowledge	**11.** peace	**16.** depend
2. reverse	**7.** favor	**12.** remark	**17.** bridge
3. afford	**8.** notice	**13.** imposs	**18.** horr
4. avoid	**9.** terr	**14.** profit	**19.** laugh
5. exchange	**10.** predict	**15.** pass	**20.** blame

Word Sort Chart

-able		-ible
1. ____________	**11.** ____________	**2.** ____________
3. ____________	**12.** ____________	**9.** ____________
4. ____________	**14.** ____________	**13.** ____________
5. ____________	**15.** ____________	**18.** ____________
6. ____________	**16.** ____________	
7. ____________	**17.** ____________	
8. ____________	**18.** ____________	
10. ____________	**19.** ____________	

At Home: Together, brainstorm more words that end with the suffixes *-able* and *-ible* and list them.

Name ______________________________

A. Write a synonym and an antonym for each vocabulary word.

1. convictions Synonym: ______________ Antonym: ______________

2. oppression Synonym: ______________ Antonym: ______________

3. remedies Synonym: ______________ Antonym: ______________

4. evident Synonym: ______________ Antonym: ______________

5. persistent Synonym: ______________ Antonym: ______________

6. defiance Synonym: ______________ Antonym: ______________

7. momentum Synonym: ______________ Antonym: ______________

8. resonated Synonym: ______________ Antonym: ______________

B. Choose six of the vocabulary words and write a sentence that includes the vocabulary word and either a synonym or antonym for it.

9. ____

10. ____

11. ____

12. ____

13. ____

14. ____

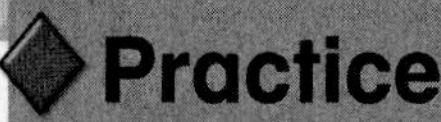

Name ______________________________

Write a paragraph summarizing an incident where you or someone you know stood up against an injustice. First use the organizer below and then write your summary.

1. Topic: ______________________________

2. Main Ideas:

a. ______________________________

____

b. ______________________________

____

c. ______________________________

____

3. Resolution: ______________________________

____

____

____

____

Write your paragraph on the lines below.

____

____

____

____

____

____

____

At Home: Have the student summarize his or her day at school.

Name ______________________________

As you read *Let It Shine: Rosa Parks,* fill in the Summary Chart.

Beginning	Middle	End

Summary

How does the information you wrote in this Summary Chart help you monitor comprehension of *Let It Shine: Rosa Parks*?

At Home: Have the student use the chart to retell the story.

Name ______________________________

As I read, I will pay attention to tempo.

In 1890 lawmakers in Louisiana passed an unusual law. It required
10 black passengers and white passengers to sit in separate railroad cars.
21 Two years later Homer Plessy sat in a car reserved for white
33 passengers. Plessy was African American. He was arrested and put on trial.
45 All court cases have a name. This one was called *Plessy v. Ferguson.*
58 The "v" stands for *versus*, the Latin word for "against."
68 Plessy's lawyer said the law was illegal. He said it violated the Fourteenth
81 Amendment to the U.S. Constitution. The Fourteenth Amendment requires
90 states to treat every citizen equally. The Louisiana law didn't do that, Plessy's
103 lawyer argued. Plessy was arrested for sitting where he wanted. White
114 passengers who sat where they wanted were not.
122 Louisiana judges ruled against Plessy. What was important to them was
133 the quality of the coaches. If "black coaches" and "white coaches" were the
146 same, they said, separating passengers by race was okay. In 1896 seven
157 members of the U.S. Supreme Court agreed with the Louisiana judges.
168 "Separate but equal" became the law of the land. Now it was legal to
182 separate black and white people in schools and other places. All the states
195 had to do was keep the quality of the segregated facilities equal. 207

Comprehension Check

1. What was Plessy's argument against segregation? **Summarize**

2. Do you think "separate but equal" would be fair if the quality of the cars was truly equal? Why or why not? **Make Judgments**

	Words Read	–	Number of Errors	=	Words Correct Score
First Read		–		=	
Second Read		–		=	

At Home: Help the student read the passage, paying attention to the goal at the top of the page.

Name ______________________________

Read the following stanza from Percy Bysshe Shelley's "Canto 6." Then analyze the poem. Look for examples of the poet's craft, such as rhyme, simile, and repetition.

from Canto 6
by Percy Bysshe Shelley

Then, rallying cries of treason and of danger
Resounded: and — 'They come! to arms! to arms!
The Tyrant is amongst us, and the stranger
Comes to enslave us in his name! to arms!'
In vain: for Panic, the pale fiend who charms
Strength to forswear her right, those millions swept
Like waves before the tempest — these alarms
Came to me, as to know their cause I leapt
On the gate's turret, and in rage and grief and scorn I wept!

____

____

____

____

____

____

____

____

____

____

____

____

____

____

At Home: Together, discuss the poem above and its meaning.

Name ______________________________

Write a sentence(s) for each word and include an example as a context clue for the word's meaning.

1. segregation ______________________________
____

2. amenities ______________________________
____

3. plight ______________________________
____

4. disgrace ______________________________
____

5. activist ______________________________
____

6. vigilantes ______________________________
____

7. discrimination ______________________________
____
____

8. boycott ______________________________
____

9. civil rights ______________________________
____

10. cases ______________________________
____

At Home: Have the students choose three words from the list above and provide additional examples as context clues.

Name ____________________

A. Complete the chart by adding the suffixes *-ant* or *-ent* and *-ance* or *-ence* to each root or base word. Use a dictionary if needed.

Root or Base Word	-ant -ent	-ance -ence
import		
indulge		
hesitate		
persist		
dominate		
tolerate		
resist		

B. Choose at least four sets of words with suffixes from the chart above and write a sentence for each set. Underline the words with suffixes in your sentences.

1. ____________________

2. ____________________

3. ____________________

4. ____________________

At Home: Help the student find other examples of words with suffixes, *-ant, -ent, -ance,* and *-ence.*

Name ______________________________

Complete each analogy by writing a parallel comparison.

1. date : chronology :: ____________ : ____________

2. bid : auction :: ____________ : ____________

3. wrath : anger :: ____________ : ____________

4. finale : debut :: ____________ : ____________

5. convictions : doubts :: ____________ : ____________

6. handshake : encounter :: ____________ : ____________

7. uttered : words :: ____________ : ____________

8. defiance : agreement :: ____________ : ____________

9. victorious : winning :: ____________ : ____________

10. swiveled : turned :: ____________ : ____________

11. dilapidated : elegant :: ____________ : ____________

12. remedies : cures :: ____________ : ____________

13. quickened : slowed :: ____________ : ____________

14. economists : economy :: ____________ : ____________

15. ruptured : burst :: ____________ : ____________

Write your own analogy. Use the given word in your analogy.

16. periodic

____________ : ____________ :: ____________ : ____________

17. shakily

____________ : ____________ :: ____________ : ____________

Name ______________________________

Use each pair of vocabulary words in a single sentence.

1. anticipated, grimaced ______________________________

2. continuous, ordeals ______________________________

3. illegally, decades ______________________________

4. dejectedly, migrant ______________________________

5. reputation, evident ______________________________

6. mistreated, nourishing ______________________________

7. instinctively, momentum ______________________________

8. participate, decrease ______________________________

9. rafters, resonated ______________________________

10. oppression, persistent ______________________________

Name ______________________________

Mark each sentence *True* or *False*. If the sentence is false, correct it to agree with the underlined word.

1. A philosopher gives medicine to patients.

2. The Renaissance movement began in England.

3. An elaborate dress might be very plain and simple.

4. If you recommend a book about architecture, you think no one should read it.

5. Many nobles commissioned art during the 1500s.

6. A miniature is a medium-sized painting.

7. An artist likely envisioned the work before she painted it.

8. If a painting has proportion, it will definitely not be realistic.

Name ______________________________

Read the generalization and the sentences that follow. Underline the sentence that does NOT support the generalization.

1. **Generalization:** Great designs last forever.

   The advances that architects made during ancient Greece and Rome are still used today.

   Many museums house artworks that are thousands of years old.

   Much of the art of ancient times has been destroyed by natural disasters.

2. **Generalization:** Architecture is the most useful of the arts.

   Architecture is used to design cities.

   It is not important how a building looks.

   Architecture dictates the design of the places we live and work.

3. **Generalization:** The Renaissance is one of the most important periods in art history.

   Many of the master artists come from the Italian Renaissance.

   America was not directly affected by the Renaissance.

   Works and methods from the Renaissance affect artists up to this day.

Write a statement that is a generalization about art or design. Then, write three sentences to support that statement.

____

____

____

____

____

____

____

At Home: Have the student read a story and make a generalization about the main character.

Name ______________________________

As you read *Leonardo's Horse* fill in the Generalizations Chart.

Important Information	Generalization

How does the information you wrote in this Generalizations Chart help you monitor comprehension of *Leonardo's Horse*?

At Home: Have the student use the chart to retell the story.

Name ____

As I read, I will pay attention to pauses, stops, and intonation.

The ancient Egyptian pyramids of Giza amaze visitors and scholars.
10 No one knows exactly how the Egyptians built these three massive
21 monuments near the city of Cairo. Made from heavy stone blocks, they
33 have perfect **proportions**. Each has four walls shaped like triangles. They
44 lean toward one another at the same angle to form the pointy top of the
59 pyramid. Unlike the floors of many old houses, the base of each pyramid
72 is level. And the walls face squarely each of the points on the compass–
86 north, south, east, and west.
91 A famous architect named Imhotep designed the very first pyramid
101 for an Egyptian king. Over 4,000 years later a well-known American
111 architect named I. M. Pei thought of the timeless shape of the pyramids
123 of ancient Egypt when he needed inspiration. Pei was designing a new
135 entrance for the great Louvre (LOOV-rah) museum in Paris, France. He
145 wanted to create an entrance that would blend with the historic museum,
157 which is hundreds of years old. But he also wanted it to look modern
171 because Paris is a modern, bustling city. Pei thought an entrance shaped
183 like a pyramid but made of glass would be perfect. Like Imhotep before
196 him, he had to overcome many obstacles before his pyramid was built. 208

Comprehension Check

1. Why are the Giza pyramids considered amazing? **Make Generalizations**

2. How is I. M. Pei's pyramid similar to Imhotep's pyramid? How are they different? **Compare and Contrast**

	Words Read	–	Number of Errors	=	Words Correct Score
First Read		–		=	
Second Read		–		=	

At Home: Help the student read the passage, paying attention to the goal at the top of the page.

Name ______________________________

When you research a topic, you will often need to consult primary sources. **Primary sources** are materials, such as journals, diaries, letters, speeches, and interviews, that come from the time and place you are researching. Journals and diaries are especially helpful for providing details about the life of the time.

Read the following excerpt from *The Diary of Samuel Pepys* that was written June 1661 in London, England. Answer the questions.

24th (Midsummer-day). We kept this a holiday, and so went not to the office at all. All the morning at home. At noon my father came to see my house now it is done, which is now very neat. He and I and Dr. Williams (who is come to see my wife, whose soar belly is now grown dangerous as she thinks) to the ordinary over against the Exchange, where we dined and had great wrangling with the master of the house when the reckoning was brought to us, he setting down exceeding high every thing. I home again and to Sir W. Batten's, and there sat a good while. So home.

1. What kind of information does the journal give? ______________________________

____

2. Why might this primary source be useful?

____

3. What do you learn from this entry?

____

____

4. Why do you think the spellings and language are different?

____

____

At Home: Talk about what kinds of things the student might record in a diary.

Words can be made up of parts, including prefixes, suffixes, and roots. Many words have **Greek roots.** Knowing root meanings will help you expand your vocabulary.

Example: philosopher = *phil* (love) + *sophia* (wisdom)

Identify a Greek root in each of the words and write the root and meaning on the first line. Use a dictionary to help. Then, use each word in a sentence. Write some more words that have the same roots.

1. cosmopolitan: ______________________________

____

____

2. bibliography: ______________________________

____

____

3. genre: ______________________________

____

____

4. telegram: ______________________________

____

____

5. chronology: ______________________________

____

____

At Home: Challenge the student to think of words with other Greek roots.

Knowing the meaning of some common **Greek and Latin prefixes** can help you figure out the meaning of many words. Here is a chart of some common prefixes and their meanings. Note that *co*, *com*, and *con* all come from the same root.

Prefix	Meaning of Prefix	Example Word	Word Meaning
co, com, con	together or with	contract	pull together
post	after	postpone	place after
pro	in front of or for	proportion	a portion in relation to a whole
sub	under	submarine	under the sea

If you do not know the meaning of a word and you forget what the prefix means, think of another word that has the same prefix. This can help you understand new words.

Read each sentence. Underline the words that contain one of the prefixes above. Use a double underline for the prefix. Then write another word that contains the same prefix on the line following the sentence.

1. Leonardo da Vinci was an artist by profession. ______________

2. He was commissioned to make many works of art. ______________

3. Artists do not have to cooperate with others. ______________

4. They do have to submit to the guidelines of the commission.

   ____

5. Sometimes works would be postponed because of an artist's health or schedule. ______________________________

At Home: Have the student make a list of words with these prefixes and use the words in sentences.

Name ______________________________

Write a context clue for each underlined vocabulary word in the sentences. You can use more than one word for your answer.

immigrated	honorable	tinkering	destination
fidget	formally	glumly	unsteady

1. Julie began tinkering with her computer settings to ______________________________

____

2. To get to our final destination, our flight included several connections, but we finally arrived at the ______________________ our journey.

3. The family immigrated and ______________________.

4. Melinda formally and ____________ introduced the queen to her parents.

5. Holding public office is an honorable position and the official should always be careful to make sure his or her ______________________

6. Our playground equipment is unsteady; when I stood on it, the bars

____

7. Rachel's mother suggested that if Rachel sat still and did not fidget and ______________ she would be more relaxed.

8. Kevin stared glumly out the window when he didn't get his way; his ______________________ soon rubbed off on all of us.

Name ________________________________

Read the following events and then number them in sequence. Then, write a story that uses the proper sequence and elaborates on the main idea.

____ Nupur builds a time machine with her friend Juan.

____ Nupur and Juan talk about building a time machine.

____ Nupur reads about time travel at school.

____ Nupur is inspired to build a time machine.

____ Nupur and Juan test their time machine.

____

____

____

____

____

____

____

____

____

____

____

____

____

____

____

____

____

At Home: Talk about a story that the student knows well. Together, list the events in the order they occur.

Name ______________________________

As you read *LAFFF* fill in the Sequence Chart.

Setting
↓
Characters
↓
Events
↓
Events
↓
Events
↓
Events

How does the information you wrote in this Sequence Chart help you monitor comprehension of *LAFFF*?

At Home: Have the student use the chart to retell the story.

Name ______________________________

As I read, I will pay attention to punctuation and characters' voices.

The three friends sat on the stone slab, talking about the most
12 important day of their lives. "Just think," said Solay. "Soon, nothing will
24 be like it was."
28 Rio put his head in his hands and scoffed. "Even without the
40 Ceremony, things are changing. For the worse."
47 As if on cue, the tall, cylindrical Regulator that towered over their
59 bench began to sputter. The three friends looked up at it in dismay. With
73 a few ticks and a buzz, it shut down. A moment later, it hummed feebly
88 back to life.
91 "See what I mean?" said Rio. The Regulators were like the lungs of
104 Village. Built centuries ago, they filtered harmful carbon dioxide from the
115 air and replenished it with fresh oxygen.
122 "Everyone knows the Regulators are breaking down," said Chenille. Of
132 the three, she was the smallest. The fingers on her delicate hands were
145 long and thin, perfect for weaving. "But the Advisers will find a way to
159 fix them. Otherwise . . . would we have to build a sky—like Dome?"
171 She glanced to her right, where Dome's glassy, round hump was just
183 visible on the horizon. "That won't work," said Solay. She was oldest of
196 the three by several months. "Dome is powered by the same source. Their
209 whole city is dying." Like most of the systems left from Time Past, no
223 records about the workings of the air purifiers had survived. 233

Comprehension Check

1. What events are the friends expecting? **Sequence**

2. What if all the Regulators stop working? **Draw Conclusions**

	Words Read	–	Number of Errors	=	Words Correct Score
First Read		–		=	
Second Read		–		=	

At Home: Help the student read the passage, paying attention to the goal at the top of the page.

Name ______________________________

You can use **keywords** and a search engine to explore the Internet and bring up a list of Web sites. You can select a Web site by clicking on the underlined words called **hyperlinks**.

Use the Web site below to answer the questions.

http://www.eaps.org/

The Edgar Allan Poe Society

Information About Poe:

General Topics About <u>Poe</u>

The <u>Works</u> of Edgar Allan Poe

A Selection of <u>Lectures and Articles</u> on Poe

Articles from <u>Poe Studies / Dark Romanticism</u>

<u>Subject Index</u> (to pages at this site)

<u>Searching</u> this site

1. Who hosts this Web site?

____

2. What keywords would you use to find this site?

____

3. Where would you find information about Poe's writing?

____

4. How could you look for information about the organization?

____

____

5. Which link would you click on to find out more about Poe's writing?

____

At Home: Together, identify some information that could be found under the General Topics about Poe.

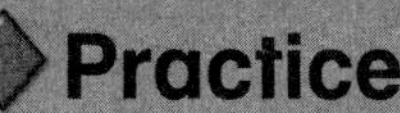

Practice

Vocabulary Strategy: Synonyms

Name ______________________________

Synonyms are words that have the same or nearly the same meaning. Many words have the same denotation (dictionary definition) but have different connotations (implied meanings). For example, the words *laugh* and *joke* can be synonyms. Both words may have negative connotations because they may suggest "a cause for derision." The words may also have positive connotations because they suggest "a cause for merriment."

Read each sentence. Write a sentence that uses a synonym that has a different connotation than the underlined word.

1. The miserly man refused to eat at the expensive restaurant.

____

____

2. The princess wore fancy jewelry to the party.

____

____

3. My curious neighbor saw an unfamiliar car parked in my driveway.

____

____

4. The picky customer inspected every shirt for tears and stains.

____

____

5. Eve ate two sandwiches for lunch every day, but she was still scrawny.

____

____

At Home: Together, write three more sentences with words that have positive and negative connotations.

Name ______________________________

Greek suffixes can be added to roots or base words to make new words. Here are some Greek suffixes that you may already know.

Suffix	Meaning of Suffix	Example Word
-logy, -ology	the study or the science of	biology
-ician	one who specializes in	physician
-crat	believer in	democrat

If you do not know the meaning of a word and you forget what the suffix means, think of another word that has the same suffix. This can help you understand new words.

Look at each root and add the Greek suffix to it, as indicated. Write the word on the line. Then use the word in a sentence of your own.

1. crimin + *-logy* ______________

____

____

2. statist + *-ician* ______________

____

____

3. auto + *-crat* ______________

____

____

4. pediatr + *-ician* ______________

____

____

At Home: Together, make a list of other words with these suffixes.

Name ______________________________

A. Answer the questions about the vocabulary words.

immense	nuisance	portable	anthropologists	presumably

1. What is a synonym of *immense*? What is an antonym?

2. Would you call a mosquito a nuisance? Explain.

3. Name three portable items.

4. Why are anthropologists interested in communication?

5. Use the vocabulary word *presumably* in a sentence of your own.

B. Write a short paragraph about communication. Try to include all the vocabulary words and underline them in your writing.

Name ______________________________

Read each problem. Then propose three possible solutions.

1. Samantha feels lonely and out of place at her new school.

2. Justin wants to play basketball but can't make Tuesday practice because of his piano lessons.

3. Kim wants a new bike but doesn't have enough money to get it.

At Home: Invite the student to identify a problem he or she has faced and tell how it was solved.

Name ______________________________

As you read *These Walls Can Talk*, fill in the Problem and Solution Chart.

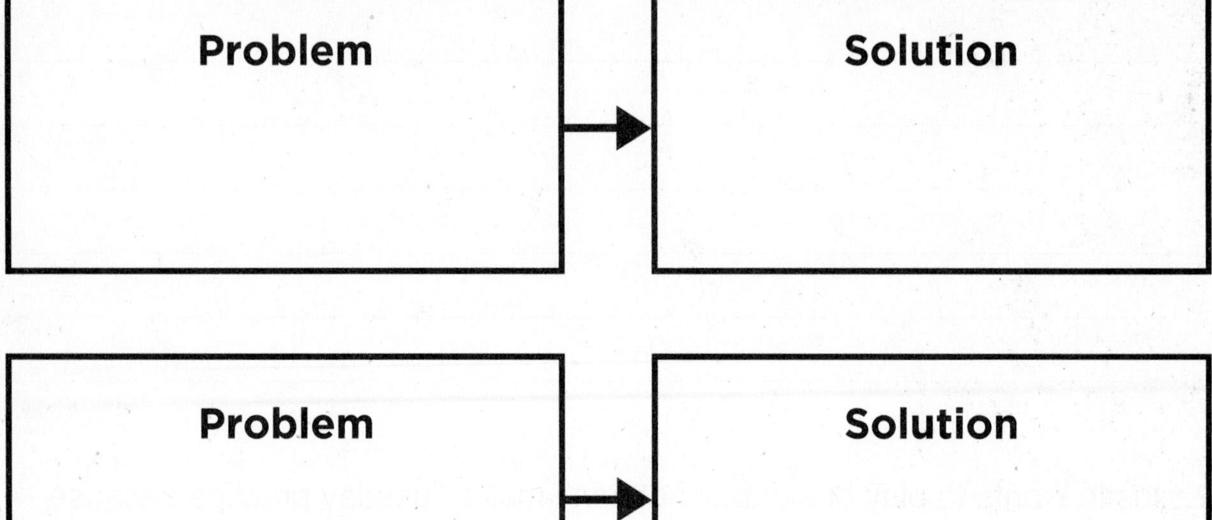

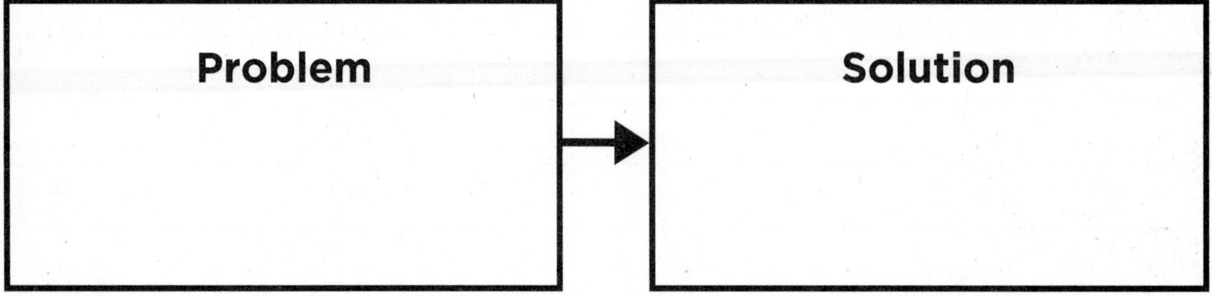

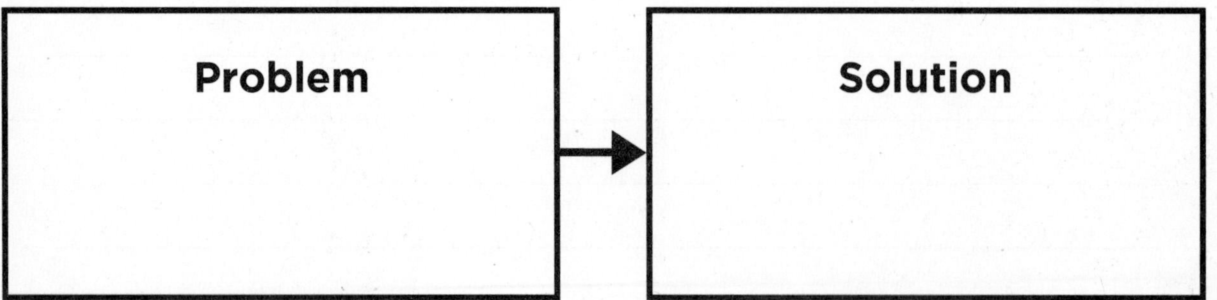

How does the information you wrote in this Problem and Solution Chart help you monitor comprehension of *These Walls Can Talk*?

At Home: Have the student use the chart to retell the story.

Name ____

As I read, I will pay attention to the pronunciation of vocabulary and other difficult words.

The Mayans were tireless builders. Most people lived in small huts made
12 from hay or limestone. However, the Mayans also built complex and
23 beautiful palaces and temples. They created tall pyramids, which rose above
34 the jungle treetops. They built temples on top of some of the pyramids.
47 Many of the Mayan stone buildings were decorated with murals and
58 carvings. Other carvings appeared on slabs of stone. Some of these carvings
70 were inscriptions written in Mayan hieroglyphics.
76 Around A.D. 900, the ancient Mayan civilization began to decline. The
86 huge cities and religious centers emptied. **Anthropologists** do not know what
97 caused this rapid decline. Scholars have suggested disease, invasion, or a
108 poor food supply. Perhaps a natural disaster, such as an earthquake, struck.
120 No one really knows.
124 In the 1500s, Spanish explorers claimed land in Central America and
134 conquered the remaining Mayans. By then, the major Mayan cities had been
146 abandoned. Jungle plants covered what were once busy social centers. These
157 plants may have saved the buildings and other artifacts from destruction by
169 the Spanish.
171 After the Spanish conquest in the 1500s, friars came to the New World.
183 Their goal was to convert people to Christianity. One of the best known of
197 these was a Franciscan priest, Diego de Landa. 205

Comprehension Check

1. What happened to Mayan civilization? What theories did anthropologists suggest? **Problem and Solution**

2. How can you tell that architecture was important to the Mayans? **Make Inferences**

	Words Read	–	Number of Errors	=	Words Correct Score
First Read		–		=	
Second Read		–		=	

At Home: Help the student read the passage paying attention to the goal at the top of the page.

Name ______________________________

Functional documents give you information to help you complete tasks, decide on purchases, or get from one place to another. They might also provide information about an organization or community. It is important to be able to interpret such documents in order to gain the information you need.

A. What if you were giving a friend instructions on how to get to your house from school? Your friend has never been to your house before. Write the directions in numbered steps for your friend.

1. ______________________________
____

2. ______________________________
____

3. ______________________________
____

4. ______________________________
____

5. ______________________________
____

B. Use the space below to draw a map of your directions.

At Home: Have the student write directions from your home to a familiar place, such as a park or community center.

Name ______________________________

Words can be made of prefixes, suffixes, and roots. Many words in the English language trace their history back to Greek and Latin. If you learn the meanings of several basic **Greek and Latin word parts**, you will unlock the key to a new English vocabulary. Knowing the basic meanings will allow you to decode the meanings of seemingly unfamiliar words.

Create ten words using the Latin and Greek word parts listed here. You can use additional prefixes and suffixes if you wish.

bene	log	tract	phono	ician	pro
graph	capit	gram	ject	co	sub
auto	bio	tele	manu	con	phys
cent	logy	crat	demo	post	agri

1. ____________________

2. ____________________

3. ____________________

4. ____________________

5. ____________________

6. ____________________

7. ____________________

8. ____________________

9. ____________________

10. ____________________

At Home: Challenge the student to give definitions for the words listed.

Name ______________________________

Absorbed prefixes describes prefixes where the final letter changes because the original form would be too hard to pronounce. You drop the last letter of the prefix and double the first letter in the base word, as in *illegal*, rather than *inlegal*. Look at the chart below for some examples.

Original Prefix and Meaning	Absorbed Forms	Sample Words
in- "not"	im-, il-, ir-	*immature, illegible, irregular*
ad- "toward"	an-, at-, ac-, ar-	*announce, attend, account, arrange*
ob- "against, toward"	oc-, op-	*occur, oppose*
con- "with"	col-, com-, cor-	*collect, commute, correct*

Read each sentence. Underline the words that have absorbed prefixes. Then write the original prefix.

1. It is sometimes difficult to immigrate to a new country when you don't know the language. ____________
2. If someone who is fluent in Spanish can accompany you, your trip will be a lot easier. ____________
3. Komal hopes to announce her graduation date next week. ____________
4. If you arrive late, give the doorman my name. ____________
5. It seems illogical not to talk when you are angry. ____________
6. The programming was irregular because of the holiday. ____________
7. My mother thinks accessories should be coordinated with an outfit.
   ____________ ____________
8. His leg was immobilized and in a cast so it could heal correctly.
   ____

At Home: Together, make a list of words with these prefixes. Use the words in sentences.

Name ______________________________

Write the clues for this completed crossword.

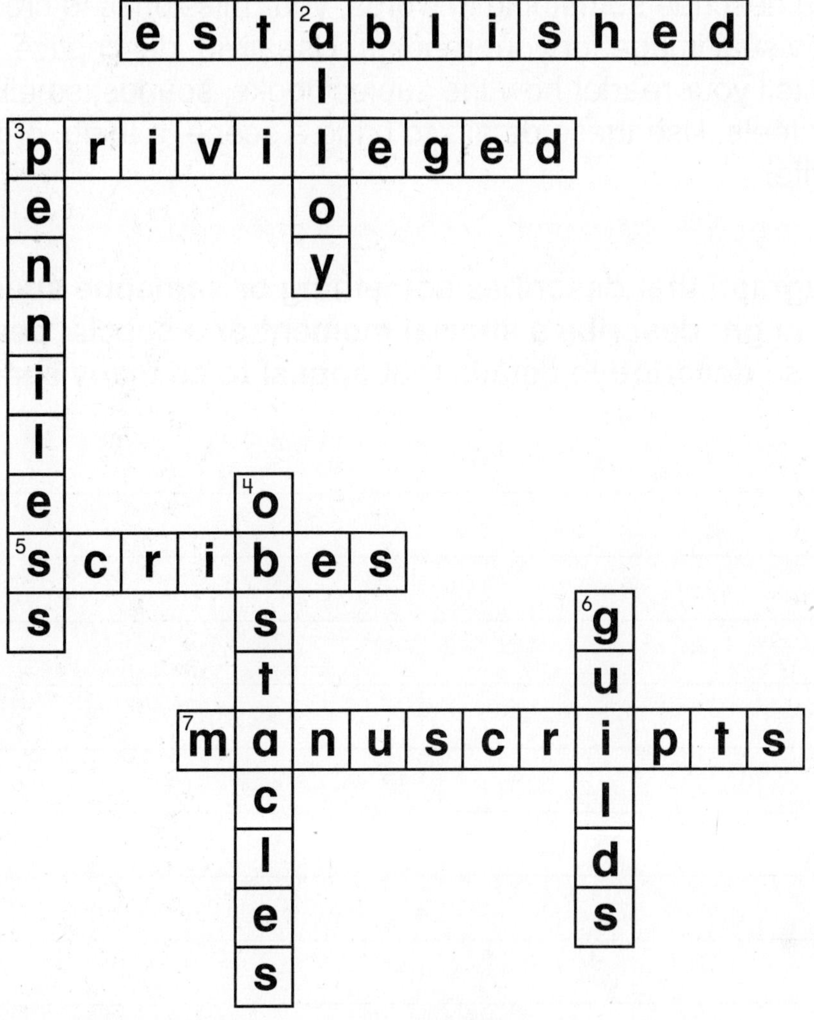

Across

1. ______________________________

3. ______________________________

5. ______________________________

7. ______________________________

Down

2. ______________________________

3. ______________________________

4. ______________________________

6. ______________________________

Name ______________________________

When you describe something in words, your mission is to create a striking visual image for your readers. Use vivid, descriptive details to tell your reader how the subject looks, sounds, smells, tastes, or feels. Use these details to bring a scene, a thing, or an event to life.

Write a paragraph that describes something or someone special to you. You might describe a special moment or a special person. Be sure to use descriptive details that appeal to as many senses as possible.

At Home: Have the student identify the senses in the paragraph.

Name ___

As you read *Breaking into Print,* fill in the Description Web.

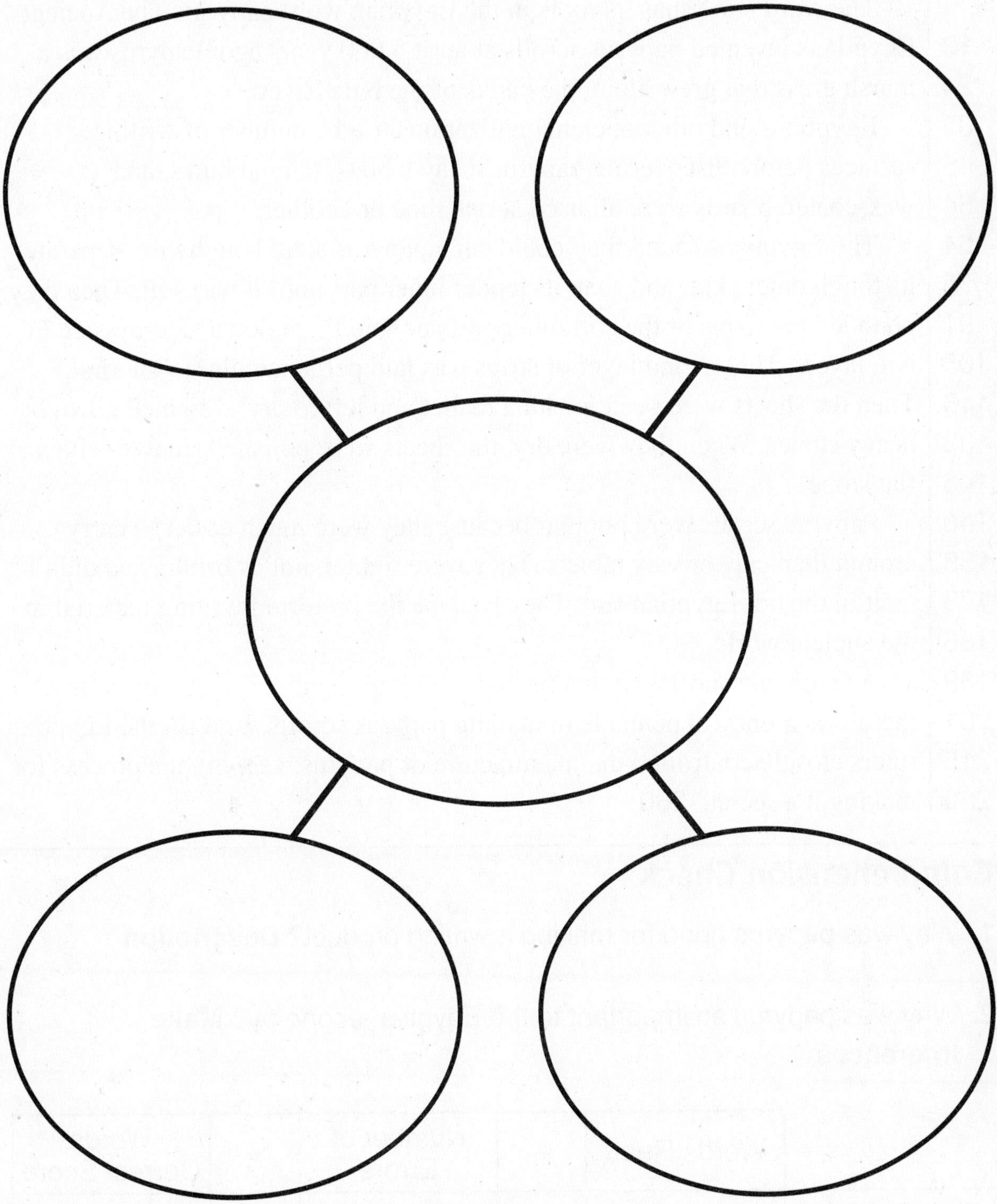

How does the information you wrote in this Description Web help you monitor comprehension of *Breaking into Print*?

At Home: Have the student use the chart to retell the story.

Name ______________________________

As I read, I will pay attention to tempo.

The word *paper* has its roots in the Egyptian word papyrus. The Ancient
13 Egyptians invented papyrus scrolls at least 5,000 years ago. Papyrus was a
24 marsh grass that grew along the banks of the Nile River.
35 Egyptians and other ancient civilizations tried a number of writing
45 surfaces before discovering papyrus. Clay tablets, animal hides, and
54 wax-coated boards were all used at one time or another.
64 The Egyptians found they could cut a papyrus stem lengthwise, separate
75 its tough outer skin, and soak its tender inner part until it was soft. Then they
91 pounded the strips of the soft inner part and laid them down side-by-side in
105 two layers. The second layer of strips was laid perpendicular to the first.
118 Then the sheets were beaten with a mallet and left to dry, weighted down by
133 heavy stones. When they were dry, the sheets were polished smooth with a
146 flat stone.
148 Papyrus scrolls were popular because they were much easier to carry
159 around than clay or wax tablets. They were lighter, not as brittle, and didn't
173 melt in the hot Egyptian sun. They became the preferred writing material in
186 the ancient world.
189 As with any substance that becomes an important part of the economy,
201 there was money to be made in making papyrus scrolls. And so, the Egyptian
215 rulers closely controlled the manufacture of papyrus, keeping the process for
226 making it a secret. 230

Comprehension Check

1. Why was papyrus good for making a writing product? **Description**

2. Why was papyrus so important to the Egyptian economy? **Make Inferences**

	Words Read	–	Number of Errors	=	Words Correct Score
First Read		–		=	
Second Read		–		=	

At Home: Help the student read the passage, paying attention to the goal at the top of the page

Name ____________________

Rhyme scheme is the pattern made by the end rhymes in the lines of a poem. Schemes are marked by lowercase letters that show which lines rhyme, such as *aabb.* Rhyme schemes create a **rhythmic pattern**, or a predictable sound, for each stanza of a poem.
Personification is a figure of speech in which human qualities are given to objects, ideas, or animals.

Read the first stanza of the poem *Sympathy* by Paul Laurence Dunbar and answer the questions.

I know what the caged bird feels, alas!
    When the sun is bright on the upland slopes;
When the wind stirs soft through the springing grass,
And the river flows like a stream of glass;
    When the first bird sings and the first bud opes,
And the faint perfume from its chalice steals—
I know what the caged bird feels!

1. What is the rhyme scheme of the poem?

____

2. The second line and the fifth line end in words that rhyme. Why?

____

____

3. Which line gives an example of personification?

____

____

4. What is this poem about?

____

____

At Home: Together, write a narrative poem that has the same rhyme scheme as Dunbar's.

Name ____

Words are made up of parts, including prefixes, suffixes, and roots. Many words have **Latin roots**. Familiarizing yourself with root meanings will help you expand your vocabulary.
Example: manuscript = *manu* (hand) + *scriptus* (written).

Read each of the following Latin roots and their definitions. Make a word using each Latin root. Then use the word in a sentence. Underline the word you use.

Root	Meaning	Example
manu	hand	
script	written	
pend	hang or weigh	
prim	first or early	
reg	rule	
vis/vid	see	

1. ____

____

2. ____

____

3. ____

____

4. ____

____

5. ____

____

At Home: Together, use the Latin roots to make a list of six more words.

Name ____________________

Words from mythology can help you understand common words you encounter daily. Some of the gods and goddesses from mythology are listed in the chart below.

A. Read the chart. Underline the words in the sentences below that are derived from the words listed in the chart.

Word from Mythology	Meaning
Ceres	goddess of grain
Jove	god of all other gods
Pan	god of goatherds, shepherds
Mars	god of war
Titan	a giant

1. I want to take martial arts classes.
2. The class was total pandemonium when the teacher left the room.
3. My father gave a jovial laugh at the thought of the joke.
4. Mom, may I have cereal for breakfast?
5. I played the lead role in the play about the Titanic.

B. Use three words based in mythology in sentences of your own.

6. ____________________

____

7. ____________________

____

8. ____________________

____

At Home: Together, discuss other words from mythology that you know.

Name ____

A. Read the paragraph below. Fill in a vocabulary word for each blank line.

dwelling	ambitious	lounge	pondering
drowsy	revived	agonized	vapors

The **(1.)** ________________ scientist studied the origin of volcanoes. He spent hours **(2.)** ________________ the possible causes. He **(3.)** ________________ over the details until he was so **(4.)** ________________ he couldn't keep his eyes open. He thought maybe the **(5.)** ________________ would hold the answer to the origin of the eruption.

B. Write a synonym, antonym, or definition for the remaining three vocabulary words.

6. ____

7. ____

8. ____

C. Choose two of the vocabulary words and use each of them in a sentence of your own.

9. ____

____

10. ____

____

Name ______________________________

The **theme** is the main idea of a story. Authors often do not state the theme directly. It is revealed through the interaction of the characters, actions, and conflict. The theme can usually be summed up in one sentence. For instance, consider the story of the tortoise and the hare. The theme of the story, which is never directly stated by the author, is "*Slow and steady wins the race.*"

Read the paragraph below. Then answer the questions.

King Minos became angry with Daedalus and imprisoned him and his son, Icarus, in a tall tower. Daedalus began planning their escape. Daedalus watched the birds fly past the tower window and was inspired to make wings for himself and his son. He made the wings out of bird feathers held together with wax. He warned his son, "Remember, Icarus, do not fly close to the sun or the wax will melt and you will fall to your death." Icarus promised. They flew away, higher and higher in the air. Icarus enjoyed flying so much that he forgot his father's words and soared up to the sun. The wax on his wings melted. He fell out of the sky to his death.

1. What is the theme of this story? ______________________________

____

____

2. What story information supports this theme? ______________________________

____

____

At Home: Together, write another story that presents the same theme.

Name ______________________________

As you read *The Dog of Pompeii,* fill in the Theme Chart.

Setting
↓
What the Characters Want
↓
Plot Problem
↓
Outcome
↓
Theme

How does the information you wrote in this Theme Chart help you monitor comprehension of *The Dog of Pompeii*?

At Home: Have the student use the chart to retell the story.

Name ____

As I read, I will pay attention to pauses and intonation.

Emilia shifted her gaze up to the craggy snow-capped mountain in
11 the distance. How majestic and peaceful Mount Etna looked! But Emilia
22 knew Mount Etna's appearance was deceptive.
28 Mount Etna had been rumbling for many months. Sometimes the
38 ground would shake. All of the villagers talked about the volcano. Some
50 of them described Mount Etna as a benign giant with an upset stomach.
63 Yes, they admitted, the volcano sometimes erupts, but it never harms anyone.
75 Other villagers remained doubtful about Mount Etna. They recounted
84 tales of an eruption hundreds of years earlier that had kept an enemy
97 army from landing in Catania, a coastal city south of Mount Etna. Well
110 then, Mount Etna's admirers would crow, doesn't that prove the volcano's
121 good intentions? Mount Etna protected the people of Sicily from invaders.
132 Emilia didn't mean to sit and **lounge**, but her thoughts wandered
143 dreamily to her favorite legends about Mount Etna. Emilia found the old
155 Greek and Roman myths as exciting then, in 1669, as they probably had
168 been long ago. She loved the myth about Mount Etna having been the
181 place where Vulcan, the god of fire and blacksmiths, had his forge. The
194 rumblings of Mount Etna were the blows of Vulcan's hammer on the
206 anvil as he busily crafted metal shields, statues, and other objects. 217

Comprehension Check

1. How does Mount Etna affect Emilia's life? **Theme**

2. What clues tell you that Mount Etna will probably erupt? **Draw Conclusions**

	Words Read	–	Number of Errors	=	Words Correct Score
First Read		–		=	
Second Read		–		=	

At Home: Help the student read the passage, paying attention to the goal at the top of the page.

Name ______________________________

Graphic aids can help you understand processes and events. Graphic aids include diagrams, charts, tables, illustrations, graphs, and photographs. Graphic aids should provide additional information and help you better understand the text.

Use the chart to answer the questions.

Cascade Eruptions During The Past 4,000 Years

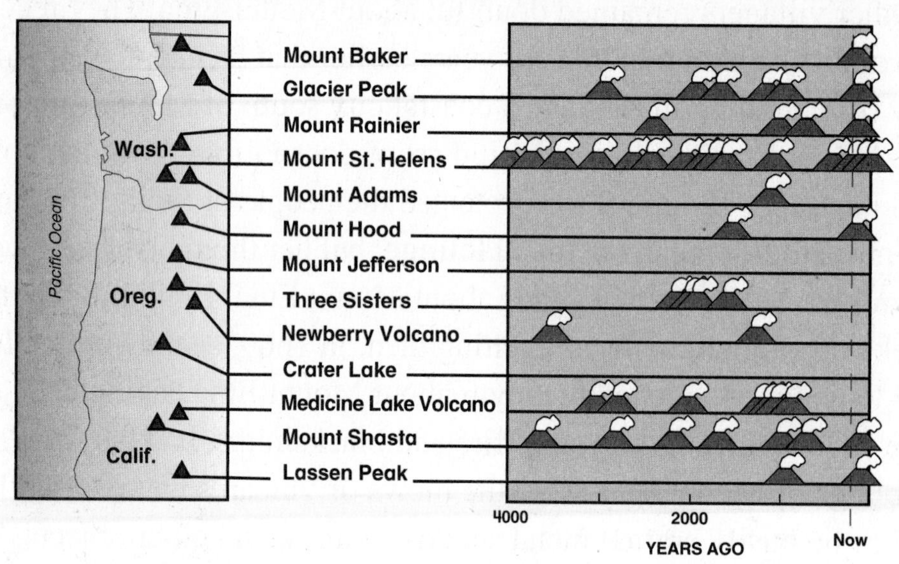

1. Which volcano has had the most eruptions? ______________________
2. Which has had the fewest eruptions? ______________________
3. How many years are covered by the chart? ______________________
4. Which volcanoes have erupted in the last 200 years?

____

____

5. Which states are shown on the chart? ______________________

____

At Home: Ask the student several questions about this chart.

Name ______________________________

Some words have more than one meaning. These are called **multiple-meaning words**. Context will usually allow you to determine which meaning of a word is being used.

Example: I grabbed a table tennis paddle to play.
We love to paddle our canoe.

Each of the words below has multiple meanings. Choose five of the words. Write two sentences for each word, using a different meaning in each sentence.

object	stand	frank	fine	content
conductor	train	general	light	

1. ______________________________
2. ______________________________
3. ______________________________
4. ______________________________
5. ______________________________
6. ______________________________
7. ______________________________
8. ______________________________
9. ______________________________
10. ______________________________

At Home: Have the student use the remaining words in sentences.

Name ______________________________

English borrows many **words from around the world**. Some of the words are cognates, or derived from a similar word in another language. Others are new words made from foreign phrases.

Use a dictionary to find the original language of each word. Tell whether it is spelled and pronounced the same or differently. Then use the word in a sentence of your own.

1. bazaar ______________________________

____

____

2. denim ______________________________

____

____

3. bronco ______________________________

____

____

4. sombrero ______________________________

____

____

5. caribou ______________________________

____

____

6. igloo ______________________________

____

____

At Home: Have the student perform the same activity with the words *gong* and *pizza*.

Name ______________________________

A. Write synonyms for each of the vocabulary words.

honorable	unsteady	portable	immense
privileged	ambitious	lounge	drowsy

1. ________________ lounge
2. ________________ drowsy
3. ________________ privileged
4. ________________ unsteady
5. ________________ ambitious
6. ________________ immense
7. ________________ honorable
8. ________________ portable

B. Answer the questions.

9. What happened during the Renaissance? ________________

____

____

10. In what class would you most likely study a philosopher? Explain.

____

____

11. What is a situation that causes you to fidget? Explain.

____

____

12. When was the last time you did something glumly?

____

____

Name ______________________________

Write a sentence for each of the vocabulary words.

recommend	envisioned	pondering	immigrated	established
destination	anthropologists	nuisance	obstacles	manuscripts

1. ______________________________

2. ______________________________

3. ______________________________

4. ______________________________

5. ______________________________

6. ______________________________

7. ______________________________

8. ______________________________

9. ______________________________

10. ______________________________